G000123866

Decision-making in Menta

Decision-making in Mental Health Review Tribunals

Elizabeth Perkins

psi

Policy Studies Institute

UNIVERSITY OF WESTMINSTER

PSI is a wholly owned subsidiary of the University of Westminster

A CIP catalogue record for this book is available from the British Library.

ISBN 0 85374 791 1
PSI Report No. 881

Typeset by MapSet Ltd, Gateshead, UK
Printed by Athenaeum Press, Gateshead, Tyne and Wear

For further information contact
Policy Studies Institute, 100 Park Village East, London NW1 3SR
Tel: 020 7468 0468 Fax: 020 7468 2211 Email: pubs@psi.org.uk

Contents

Acronyms

CPN	Community Psychiatric Nurse
ESRC	Economic and Science Research Council
MHA	Mental Health Act
MHAC	Mental Health Act Commission
MHRTs	Mental Health Review Tribunals
MTA	Mental Treatment Act
RMOs	Responsible Medical Officers
SHO	Senior House Officer
SI	Statutory Instrument

Acknowledgements

In the conduct of this research we are indebted to many people: the patients who allowed us access to their tribunals; the tribunal members who allowed us to observe their practice; and to the clerks who eased our way through the complex system of negotiating access. Karen Vale provided extensive assistance at a time when the tribunal administration was under great pressure and we are particularly indebted to the tribunal chairmen who supported this research.

Dr Sube Banerjee, at the Department of Health, has provided a source of support throughout this project. As a research manager he has been sensitive to the challenges of undertaking research, borne delays with patience and perhaps most importantly, maintained an interest in the progress of the research.

Thanks are also due to the people who have worked on the study. Data were collected by Isobel Allen, Ruth Haydon, Trevor Jones, Tim Newburn and Mike Shiner. The interviews were conducted by Marion Kumar. Data collection and analysis were undertaken by Sue Arthur, James Nazroo and Liz Perkins. Liz Perkins was responsible for the writing of the report.

A number of people have provided individual and personal support through the writing of this report. Particular thanks are due to Isobel Allen who has in her own inimitable style lightened the business of writing with her humour, concern and endless stream of 'news'. Finlay Scott has been a journeyman on the last stage of this endeavour. He has provided love and support and an endless stream of enthusiasm and encouragement.

1

Introduction

Mental Health Review Tribunals (MHRTs) were established under the Mental Health Act 1959 (MHA 1959) as a safeguard to ensure that patients are not unjustifiably or unlawfully detained in hospital. In essence they provide patients with a mechanism for appealing against detention in hospital. Criticisms of the operation of tribunals began to emerge some ten years later. Regional variations in discharge rates and questions about their powers and procedures (Greenland, 1970; Gostin, 1975; Fennell, 1977) undermined the assumptions upon which tribunals had been established. In 1983, a new Mental Health Act (MHA 1983) was passed. The MHA 1983 consolidated previous legislation and, by reducing the lengths of detention periods, increasing the opportunities to apply to MHRTs, and providing for automatic reviews, was generally associated with increasing the rights of detained patients. In addition, there were some revisions to the discharge criteria and an extension of legal aid to cover the costs of legal representation.

Throughout the 1990s mental health services came under an ever brighter spotlight. Homicides and suicides by people with mental disorder have led to demands for more stringent controls. Successive governments have responded to growing public fears of a 'failing mental health system' by bolting new statutes on to existing legislation. Since 1994, there have been a number of policy documents designed to deal with the ever more complex problem of providing mental health services in community-based settings.

Supervision registers[1] were introduced in October 1994 to help to prevent people at risk from 'falling through the care network'. These registers, designed to identify and track patients with severe mental illness, were viewed in *The Report of the Inquiry into the Care and Treatment of Christopher Clunis* (Ritchie *et al.*, 1994) as a useful tool. However, although initially welcomed with caution, they have been criticised for duplicating work and impinging on an individual's civil liberties. Critics also suggest that bad providers will produce bad registers, and that good providers do not need them in any case (Crepaz-Kay, 1994).

The Mental Health (Patients in the Community) Act 1995 (Department of Health, 1995) aimed to provide practitioners with new powers to enable statutory care under supervision for patients no longer detained in hospital under a section of the MHA 1983. It legalised community treatment orders but relied on a return to hospital for enforcement.

Modernising Mental Health Services (Department of Health, 1998) outlined the government's strategy for improving the way in which services respond to people with a mental disorder. This report portrayed the goal of mental health services as the provision of services that are: safe – protecting the public and providing effective care for those with mental illness when they need it; sound – ensuring that patients and service users have access to the full range of services that they need; and supportive – working with patients and service users, their families and carers to build healthy communities.

The Mental Health National Service Framework (Department of Health, 1999a) builds on *Modernising Mental Health Services*. It identifies standards designed to improve the quality of mental health services and reduce regional variation in provision.

As larger numbers of people with a mental disorder are being cared for outside the hospital, the appropriateness of existing mental health legislation with its emphasis on care in hospital has come under greater scrutiny. In recognition of the limits of existing mental health legislation with its roots in a framework devised over 40 years ago, the government announced in 1998 a review of the 1983 Act. The review had been planned in a number of phases; the first of which involved a scoping review, chaired by Professor Genevra Richardson, of the areas where changes to legislation were needed. This was published (Report of the Expert Committee, 1999) alongside the government's proposals for the reform of the MHA 1983 (Department of Health, 1999b; 2000).

The Green Paper (Reform of the Mental Health Act 1983, Department of Health, 1999b) endorsed the recommendation made by the Richardson Committee that a new Act should be underpinned by principles embedded within the Act to aid interpretation. It was envisaged that principles covering the following key areas would underpin the new legislation:

- Informal care and treatment should always be considered before recourse to compulsory powers.
- Patients should be involved as far as possible in the process of developing and reviewing their own care and treatment plans.
- The safety of both the individual patient and the public are of key importance in determining the question of whether compulsory powers should be imposed.
- Where compulsory powers are used, care and treatment should be located in the least restricted setting consistent with the patient's best interests and safety, and safety of the public.

In June 2002, the government published a 'Draft Mental Health Bill'. The bill begins with an outline of some of the general principles to be fleshed out in a code of practice not yet developed. The general principles to be adhered to are as follows:

- patients are involved in the making of decisions;
- decisions are made fairly and openly; and

- the interference to patients in providing medical treatment to them and the restrictions imposed in respect of them during that treatment are kept to the minimum necessary to protect their health and safety or other persons.

The scope of the proposed new Act is wide-ranging, introducing a single definition of mental disorder, new conditions under which compulsory assessment, care and treatment may take place, new mental health and mental health appeal tribunals and new safeguards for informal patients with long-term incapacity who cannot consent to treatment but are not resisting it. These proposals will be discussed briefly in Chapter 10 in relation to the findings of this study.

Background to the research

In 1984 Peay carried out a study of MHRTs. The study was designed to examine the operation of MHRTs within the context of the then new MHA 1983. In her research, Peay carefully demonstrates how the law is used to resolve the conflict between an individual's interests and that individual's rights. In doing so, she highlights that the 'quality of safeguard which tribunals represent depends both on the substance of the law and those who apply it'.

The present study was commissioned by the Department of Health 12 years later. It was designed to investigate the way in which MHRTs made decisions in relation to patients detained under section 2 and section 3 of the MHA 1983. Section 2 of the Act authorises compulsory admission to hospital of a patient for assessment and detention for a period up to 28 days. It is not possible to renew a section 2; if it is considered desirable that the patient remains in hospital the patient must either agree to stay as an informal patient or fulfil the criteria for admission to hospital under section 3 of the Act. Section 3 of the Act allows a patient to be compulsorily admitted to hospital for treatment and detained for an initial period of up to six months. The authority to detain a patient under this section can be renewed. The research was commissioned to examine only those tribunals dealing with non-restricted patients[2]; other work had been funded by the Home Office to explore the detention of restricted patients. The study broadly parallels that of Peay's; using similar methods but differing in the sample size and composition.

The study was initially planned in two inter-related stages – a study of MHRT decision-making; and a study of what happened to patients once they were discharged. Within the second stage, matched samples of patients discharged by responsible medical officers (RMOs) and tribunals were followed up over a nine-month period. Details of this second study will be published shortly.

Chapter 2 examines the legal background to detention and the organisation and power of tribunals. Chapter 3 describes the way in which the study was conducted. Chapter 4 looks at the roles of members and is based mainly on data drawn from interviews with tribunal members, together with relevant examples from the data drawn from the non-participant observation of tribunals. Chapters 5, 6, 7 and 8 deal with the decision-making process as it develops in the three stages of the tribunal: the pre-hearing meeting, the hearing and the deliberation. These chapters are based on both observation and interview data. Chapter 5 addresses the way in which the decision-making process begins in the pre-hearing meeting. It explores the conduct of the meeting and the content of the discussions. Chapter 6 discusses the hearing itself, in which the RMO and patient provide evidence. Chapter 7 and Chapter 8 provide details of the way in which decisions are made; the process by which members reach their decision is described separately from the way in which the statutory criteria are used in decision-making. Chapter 9 focuses on the statement of reasons and examines the relationship between the reasons and the observed deliberations. Chapter 10 discusses the findings of the research, with a short analysis of their implications for a new Mental Health Act.

Notes

1 (HSG(94)5).

2 Patients fall into two groups – restricted and non-restricted. Restricted patients are those where the Crown court has made a hospital order in respect of an offender, including that the offender shall be subject to the restrictions set out under section 41 of the MHA 1983. Restricted patients are dealt with differently within the MHA 1983 and by tribunals.

2

Legal Background to Detention

Tribunals of many different types have been established throughout the twentieth century. They exist to provide simpler, speedier, cheaper and more accessible justice than ordinary courts. The Franks Committee (Report of the Committee, 1957) suggested that tribunals 'should properly be regarded as machinery provided by Parliament for adjudication rather than as part of the machinery of administration'. Leggatt (2001) reinforces this point stating that 'Tribunals are an alternative to court, not administrative, processes' and will keep the confidence of users 'only in so far as they are able to demonstrate similar qualities of independence and impartiality to the courts'. Tribunals are based on the premise that a group of independent people, from different backgrounds and with comparable status, applying their minds to a problem will produce better decisions than any individual. Tribunals have evolved over time, giving rise to diverse models (Wade and Forsyth, 1994), but they have some common elements:

- independence of administration;
- capacity to reach a binding decision;
- decisions reached by a panel of members;
- procedures not dissimilar to those of courts of law;
- permanent existence.

It is important to remember that tribunals have, in substance, the same functions as courts of law – they find facts and apply legal rules to them impartially. In the case of Mental Health Review Tribunals (MHRTs), however, this is a complex task.

MHRTs are independent judicial bodies established under the Mental Health Act 1959 (MHA 1959). They provide patients with a mechanism for appealing against detention in hospital. A hearing only takes place when the patient's doctor has declined to discharge the patient and therefore, by definition, any tribunal decision to discharge a patient is usually against the advice of the patient's doctor. The patient and 'nearest relative' (section 26, MHA 1983) are both given the opportunity to have their case reviewed by a panel independent of the hospital in which the patient is detained. MHRTs are only one way by which detained patients can be discharged from section. In practice, most detained patients will be discharged by their consultant.

MHRTs comprise a medical member, a legal member (referred to as the tribunal president) and a lay member (see Chapter 4 for a more detailed discussion of roles). Until the Mental Deficiency Act 1913 (MDA 1913), there was a strong judicial involvement in the process of detaining and discharging all persons considered to have a mental disorder. Compulsion was initiated by medical practitioners but regulated by justices of the peace. Medical superintendents were required to make regular returns to justices of the peace on the state and condition of all patients compulsorily detained in their hospitals under the Lunacy Act 1890/91. The justices inspected the superintendent's returns and were able to direct the discharge of any persons who appeared to be fit for discharge.

By 1957, new procedures instituted for compulsion or certification removed the need for legal authorisation to detain a person in hospital on the grounds of mental disorder. The Royal Commission in 1957 decided that:

> *To refer the application and medical recommendations to a justice of the peace before the patient's admission would not ... provide a significant additional safeguard for the patient.*

In the absence of judicial involvement in the removal of civil liberties, there was a recognised need for a new body that would:

> *give patients the opportunity to have the use of compulsion investigated by a strong independent body comprising both medical and non-medical members.* [Royal Commission, 1957]

The Commission stated that the review tribunals would not be acting as an appellate court of law, considering whether the initial detention had been justified or whether there was some technical flaw in the documents authorising admission. Instead, the review tribunal's function would be:

> *to consider the patient's mental condition at the time when it considers his application, and to decide whether the type of care which has been provided by the use of the compulsory powers is the most appropriate to his present needs, or whether any alternative form of care might now be appropriate, or whether he could now be discharged from care altogether.*

In describing this approach, the Minister of Health explained during the Parliamentary debate on 5 May 1959 that they had been looking for:

> *[a] structure which would reflect the balance of the considerations we must have in mind. They are firstly the liberty of the subject, secondly, the necessity of bringing treatment to bear where treatment is required and can be beneficial to the individual, and thirdly, the consideration of the protection of the public.*

The current procedure for dealing with tribunal applications is set out in the 1983 Mental Health Review Tribunal Rules (1983 Rules). Where the 1983 Rules are silent on a point of procedure, Jones states that the tribunal must follow rules of natural justice, that is, it should act in an unbiased way and provide an opportunity for each party to state his case adequately (Jones, 1997, p. 240).

Under the MHA 1983, tribunals are empowered to review all cases of patients who have been detained. Detained patients can apply to a tribunal within the first 14 days of being detained under section 2[1]; and once only within each six-month period of detention under section 3[2]. The nearest relative can also appeal on behalf of a detained person. The MHA 1983 imposes upon hospital managers the duty to refer to a tribunal any patient detained under section 3 of the Act who has not had a tribunal hearing in the first six months of detention and, in addition, any patient detained for three years (one year in the case of children under the age of 16). Thus, patients who lack the ability or initiative to make an application to a tribunal have an automatic independent review. This provides a safeguard for long-term detained patients who do not apply on their own behalf.

Organisation of tribunals

At the time of the fieldwork for this study, tribunals were organised nationally into eight regions, replicating those of the regional offices of the NHS Executive. There has recently been a reduction in the number of regions (SI 1998 No. 1460). Each region is presided over by a regional chairman who is ultimately accountable to the Lord Chancellor's Office. Each regional chairman is both autonomous and independent. In the past, this resulted in regional differences in the operation of tribunals. At the time of the study, this was beginning to change, with the adoption of a more consistent national approach. The regional differences in tribunal procedure, particularly in the training of members, that were observed in this study, have become less pronounced as a result of closer collaboration between the regional chairmen.

The tribunal is independent of the hospital and the detaining authorities. However, the hearings take place in the hospital (or other accommodation) where the patient is detained. The Department of Health is responsible for the administration and running of the tribunals in England through regional offices. Each office employs tribunal clerks and administrative staff whose functions include arranging the hearings, the administration of the reports, processing tribunal members' expenses, and clerking and ensuring the smooth running of the tribunal. The Department of Health is responsible for the resourcing of the tribunals but they are independent of the Department of Health and the Home Office.

Powers of the tribunal

The powers to discharge a patient derive from section 72 of the MHA 1983:

> (1) Where application is made to a Mental Health Review Tribunal by or in respect of a patient who is liable to be detained under this Act, the tribunal

may in any case direct that the patient be discharged, and –

(a) the tribunal shall direct the discharge of a patient liable to be detained under section 2 above if they are satisfied –
    (i) that he is not then suffering from mental disorder or from mental disorder of a nature or degree which warrants his detention in hospital for assessment (or for assessment followed by a medical treatment) for at least a limited period; or
    (ii) that his detention as aforesaid is not justified in the interests of his own health or safety or with a view to the protection of other persons;
(b) the tribunal shall direct the discharge of a patient liable to be detained otherwise than under section 2 above if they are satisfied –
    (i) that he is not then suffering from mental illness, psychopathic disorder, severe mental impairment or mental impairment or from any of those forms of disorder of a nature or degree which makes it appropriate for him to be detained in a hospital for medical treatment; or
    (ii) that it is not necessary for the health or safety of the patient or for the protection of other persons that he should receive such treatment; or
    (iii) in the case of an application by virtue of paragraph (g) of section 66(1) above, that the patient, if released, would not be likely to act in a manner dangerous to other persons or to himself.

(2) In determining whether to direct the discharge of a patient detained otherwise than under section 2 above in a case not falling within paragraph (b) of subsection (1) above, the tribunal shall have regard –

(a) to the likelihood of medical treatment alleviating or preventing a deterioration of the patient's condition; and
(b) in the case of a patient suffering from mental illness or severe mental impairment, to the likelihood of the patient, if discharged, being able to care for himself, to obtain the care he needs or to guard himself against serious exploitation.

If the tribunal is satisfied on either of these questions then it has a duty to discharge the patient. At the time this study was undertaken it was up to the patient to prove to the tribunal that he or she satisfied the criteria. However, following a landmark ruling in 2001[3] this is no longer the situation. It is generally considered that the standard of proof required is on the balance of probabilities (Eldergill, 1998).

The statutory criteria are discussed in more detail in subsequent chapters. However, in her study of tribunals Peay notes that as the criteria are phrased in the negative, they 'merely concern themselves with what may not be done to individuals and represent the law's interest in achieving a form of negative substantive justice' (Peay, 1989, p. 17).

Tribunal outcomes

An MHRT has a number of options when making its decision. It can decide to:

(i) discharge someone from section immediately;
(ii) defer discharge until a stated date to allow time for community care arrangements to be put in place; or
(iii) not discharge.

If the tribunal decides not to discharge, it may choose to recommend to the hospital that the patient be transferred to a different hospital, or to a particular treatment plan. The tribunal also has the option of considering the case further in the event of non-compliance with recommendations. The tribunal does not, however, have any powers to enforce its recommendations.

The tribunal has to give a written account of the decision it has reached. The tribunal *Guide for Members* (1996b) states:

> *reasons need not be elaborate but they must deal with the substantial points that have been raised and must show the parties the basis on which the tribunal has acted. It is not sufficient merely to repeat the statutory grounds. It is not usually necessary to review the evidence at length. It is important to say which evidence has been accepted and often which has been rejected. It is not usually necessary to give the reasons for acceptance or rejection of evidence.*

It is important to recognise that, as stated previously, a hearing only takes place when the patient's doctor has declined to discharge the patient. Consequently, any tribunal decision to discharge a patient is usually against the advice of the patient's doctor. There is nothing to stop a doctor re-sectioning the patient once the tribunal has discharged the patient. In addition, patients may appeal against the tribunal's decision within 14 days of the outcome.

Stages of the tribunal

The tribunal process is divided into three stages: a pre-hearing meeting; the hearing; and the deliberation. The first and last stages are closed sessions to enable the three members to discuss the case. During the hearing, evidence is heard from a number of different people. Figure 2.1 shows the typical set up and seating plan of a hearing.

Participants

It is usually expected that the patient will attend the tribunal. However, the rules allow the tribunal to proceed in the patient's absence (SI 942, Rule 21 (4)).

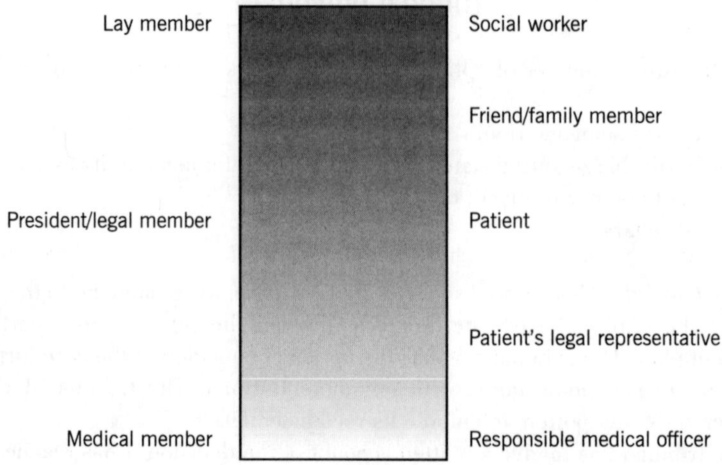

Figure 2.1 *A typical positioning of a tribunal hearing*

Non-attendance by patients at their own tribunals occasionally happens where the section is being automatically reviewed. The patient is entitled to representation. The patient may appoint any person 'whom he has authorised for that purpose' as long as they are not 'liable to be detained or subject to guardianship under the Act or a person receiving treatment for mental disorder at the same hospital or mental nursing home as the patient' (SI 942, Rule 10(1)). In practice, the vast majority of patients have legal representatives for whom they are entitled to claim legal aid.

A representative of the hospital must always attend: this is usually the patient's consultant psychiatrist or responsible medical officer (RMO). An approved social worker is also usually present: this may be the person who first applied the section or may be a newly appointed key worker for the patient. The social worker attending the hearing is usually the person who writes the social report.

Others present may include a ward nurse, sometimes in a supporting or a restraining role only, family members, or friends of the applicant. Occasionally, a community psychiatric nurse may attend and, if requested by the patient, an independent clinical psychologist or psychiatrist.

In addition to oral evidence, written reports are submitted. The procedure for submission of reports differs slightly for section 2 and section 3 hearings. For section 2, because tribunals have to be organised and heard within seven days of application, reports are usually provided on the day of the hearing. For section 3, written reports from the RMO and social worker are requested when the tribunal office receives the patient's application. Members are selected on the basis of availability. Once selected, they are sent the reports. As this may be several weeks before the actual hearing, the patient's condition may have changed by the time of the tribunal.

Neither the patient nor the patient's legal representative is asked to provide reports to be circulated in advance along with those of the RMO and the social worker. The case presented to the members through the reports does not include the patient's perspective.

Operation of tribunals

The annual number of tribunal applications has risen dramatically since the MHA 1983. In 1984, there were 3,445 applications, rising to a total of 14,913 in 1996[4] (Department of Health, 1996a). The total number of applications and references in 2000 was 20,157 (Department of Health, 2002). The number of hearings has also risen at approximately the same rate, from 2,133 in 1984 to 7,575 in 1996 (Department of Health, 1996a). There were 11,535 hearings in 2000 (Department of Health, 2002). There are approximately five times more applications for tribunal hearings from non-restricted patients than restricted patients (excluding section 2 hearings) and many more applications from the NHS and independent hospitals than from the special hospitals. Section 2 cases accounted for 2,629 hearings held in 1996, and non-restricted section 3 and section 37 cases accounted for 3,726 hearings and 1,220 hearings respectively in 1996 (Department of Health, 1996a). In 2000 there were 3,380 section 2 hearings and 6,434 non-restricted section 3 and section 37 hearings (personal communication, Department of Health 2002).

During this study, the tribunal offices were under immense pressure. The increasing volume of work was beginning to raise concerns about the implications, for tribunal members, of unclerked hearings. In addition, cancellations were increasing and were held responsible for administrative difficulties and low morale. Organising a tribunal is time consuming and resource intensive. In 1994, Blumenthal and Wessely calculated that tribunals cost some £12.3m per annum. A tribunal cancelled days before its scheduled hearing is administratively costly. Hearings are cancelled or aborted for a range of reasons. According to the Mental Health Review Tribunal Report (2002) 6 per cent of all tribunal applications in 2000 were withdrawn by the patient or discharged by the RMO. Of all applications, 22 per cent were cancelled because patients were discharged by the hospitals prior to the hearing.

Notes

1 Section 2 of the Act authorises compulsory admission to hospital of a patient for assessment and detention for a period up to 28 days. It is not possible to renew a section 2.

2 Section 3 of the Act allows a patient to be compulsorily admitted to hospital for treatment and detained for an initial period of up to six months. The authority to detain a patient under this section can be renewed.

3 In March 2001 a case was made that section 72(1) and section 73(1) of the Mental Health Act 1983 were incompatible with article 5(1)(4) of the European Convention

for the Protection of Human Rights and Fundamental Freedoms. The concept of burden of proof and the applicable test for discharge were found to be inseparable and the failure of the 1983 Act to require a tribunal to discharge a patient, where it could not be shown that he suffered from a mental disorder warranting detention, amounted to unlawful detention and infringed a person's liberty (*R.* (on the application of H) v. *Mental Health Review Tribunal, North and East London Region* [2001] H.R.L.R. 36).

4 Figures for England and Wales and includes section 2 and section 3 restricted and non-restricted applications.

3

Methods

The aim of the study was to describe and analyse the processes by which decisions are made in MHRTs. Data were collected from 61 tribunals in four of the regions in England. Observations started in December 1996 and were completed by the end of May 1997. In addition to the observational data, documentation pertaining to the observed tribunals was analysed and in-depth interviews were carried out with 24 tribunal members.

Studying decision-making

Peay, in her book *Tribunals on Trial* (1989), highlights the problem of studying legal decision-making. She states that 'the traditional view of decision-making assumed that only legally significant variables, such as the facts of the case, governed decisions, whilst the law could be viewed as a constant and the personality of the decision-maker an irrelevance (Peay, 1989, p. 21). Peay goes on to demonstrate both with reference to her own work and that of others (for example Hogarth, 1971 and Simon, 1971) that the preconceived attitudes and knowledge of decision-makers about the case under consideration frequently transform inordinately complex decisions into comparatively straightforward choices (Peay, 1989).

We knew, therefore, before the study began, that the research methods needed to be sensitive to the role played by each individual tribunal member as well as to the nature of the evidence and the legal framework within which decisions were made. In many respects, the study methods mirrored those used by Peay: data were collected by observation, interview and documentary analysis. This study, however, departs from that of Peay's in several notable respects:

- Observation was the central plank of this study design.
- In-depth interviews were carried out with tribunal members to explore a range of influences on their decision-making.
- The study focused solely on decisions concerning non-restricted patients.

Non-participant observation

The adopted approach was based on the principles of ethnography. Atkinson and Hammersley (1998) identify four key features of ethnographic methods:

(i) emphasis on exploring the nature of particular social phenomena;
(ii) tendency to work primarily with unstructured data;
(iii) investigation of a small number of cases;
(iv) analysis of data that involves explicit interpretation of the meanings and functions of human actions, the product of which mainly takes the form of verbal descriptions and explanations with quantification and statistical analysis playing a subordinate role at most.

In choosing to conduct this study using non-participant observation techniques, it was recognised that there was a well-recorded[1] set of methodological and analytical problems to be addressed, the most frequently cited being those of subjectivity, selectivity and an introduction of bias similar to the experimental effect known as the Hawthorne effect. On the basis that researchers observing any activity begin to influence what is being researched, we anticipated recording a higher standard of decision-making than that which might exist in unobserved settings.

We were not able to take any type of recording instrument into the tribunal proceedings. We therefore had to decide how to capture the dynamics, content and interactions between the members, patients and witnesses while accurately recording the proceedings but changing the observed world as little as possible.

What was initially planned as a purely qualitative study subsequently developed along the lines of positivistic research as we sought to produce rigorously collected data. Thus, in many ways the observations departed from the classical contexts of sociology and anthropology from which the technique emanated and has since grown.

Piloting of methods

There was an early and intensive investment in piloting different methods of recording observations. Three main techniques were tested:

(i) grid technique;
(ii) focused observation;
(iii) contemporaneous narrative record.

Grid technique

The grid technique for recording information offered the advantage of a tool that would reduce or remove the subjectivity and selectivity of each individual researcher.

A grid was developed following tuition from an expert in observational methods based at the Methodology Institute[2], Dr Martin Bauer. We experimented with a range of grids using predefined categories to limit the field of observation. These categories were based on information about key players or themes in the tribunal. At set time intervals the presence or absence of key pieces of information was recorded.

The use of a grid appeared to have a number of advantages. It reduced the field of observation to a small number of areas defined in advance of the hearing and enabled a more structured and focused analysis of the data. However, in practice there were a number of drawbacks:

- It did not provide sufficient information on which to base an analysis of the processes by which decisions were made.
- It enabled only a partial record of the tribunal to be taken.
- The successful development of the grid depended on being able to identify key relevant categories. There was no comprehensive body of research from which these key issues could be identified with certainty as to their accuracy. Indeed, had this body of knowledge *a priori* existed there would presumably have been little need for the study to be undertaken.

Grids may be an appropriate research tool for observations in highly structured settings, such as mechanised factory floors, where the aim of observational recording is to understand variation in relatively uniform structured practices. However, grids are not a sophisticated enough research tool to record the conversational dynamics in settings such as tribunal hearings.

Focused observation

In an attempt to build on work previously carried out by other researchers (Adler and Adler, 1994; Fasschnach, 1982) and in the belief that a narrow field of observation would improve the accuracy of the data recorded, we also piloted a grid based on five key areas. These were developed from Greenland's study of tribunals (1970). Greenland identified five key questions to guide the recording of the tribunal proceedings:

(i) Was the applicant, patient or relative given a full opportunity to present him/herself and his/her case in the best possible manner?
(ii) Did the tribunal establish the accuracy of the statements made by the detaining authority?
(iii) Was the applicant given any opportunity to refute any allegations made about him/her?
(iv) Was the conduct of the tribunal designed to protect rather than undermine the future relations between the patient and the doctor?
(v) Were the proceedings conducted with dignity, impartiality and proper concern for the liberty of the individual?

These grids were designed to capture narrative data in the form of quotes. Nine broad headings were identified to provide answers to questions i–v above. This method required researchers to think analytically while at the same time recording the information as it was generated.

There were a number of problems. Some of the headings were too broad and researchers were unable to group data consistently under the same headings. At a practical level, different sections of the grid were completed at different rates, making the physical management of pages a problem. In short, we found that we could not devise a simple grid sophisticated enough to deal with the number of variables which seemed to be relevant to the way in which decisions were being made. During the piloting of the grids we became aware of the importance of the material we were *not* collecting.

Contemporaneous narrative accounts

Contemporaneous narrative accounts sit at the opposite end of the observational spectrum to grids. In the piloting process it seemed an obvious development to examine whether an observer could achieve a comprehensive account of the tribunal from the pre-hearing meeting through to the deliberation. This technique offered the advantage of enabling us to record the broadest observational field, building up notational records of participants, interactions, routines, rituals, temporal elements, interpretations and social organisation as suggested by Hammersley and Atkinson (1983). Researchers therefore became sophisticated recording instruments, recording dialogue, key facial and emotional expressions and body language.

Despite the physical drawbacks of taking a contemporaneous narrative account, most notably aching wrists and bent backs, it was decided that this method should be piloted in more depth. Indeed, the data generated through this method was both richer and deeper than that elicited through the other methods.

A total of eight tribunals were observed and from those observations a way of proceeding in the main stage was developed (see Appendix 1 for pilot statistics).

Main stage tribunal observations

We recorded our observations by taking a full verbatim account of the proceedings. This meant that, for the purposes of analysis, we had a full account of all issues or interactions that might have a bearing on the decision-making. It also allowed us to minimise the risk of observer bias associated with selective or focused observational recording. In addition, it produced transcripts capable of being analysed by the team of researchers rather than only by the individual who had observed the tribunal. This method also had the advantage that the complete unabridged accounts were available should disputes over interpretation or the accuracy of events ever arise.

For each tribunal, standard information was recorded. This included the timings of each key stage, those present, and background information from the reports presented about the patient. This information was recorded separately from the transcripts of the proceedings (see Appendix 2 for details).

The majority of observations were carried out by one researcher on their own, to minimise intrusion and costs. We used a number of techniques to enhance the validity of the observations:

- Piloting of our methods.
- To counter suggestions of subjectivity and selectivity, a small number of tribunals in each region was observed by two observers. Accounts were then cross-checked for accuracy of recording and interpretation. We found a high degree of congruence between the accounts recorded, with very little inter-rater divergence.
- A team of six observers carried out the observations: three men and three women.
- In-depth interviews were carried out with a sample of tribunal members to collect additional data as well as to provide insights into the perceived 'authenticity' of the observed tribunals – the interviews were designed to elicit the member's account of being a tribunal member.

Each observer recorded a contemporaneous account of everything that was said, with the exception of individuals' names that were not recorded on the tribunal transcripts. In the main, this was straightforward because tribunals operated on the principle that only one person should speak at a time. Not surprisingly, there were instances in which emotional outbursts and disputes arose which supplanted this order.

Nature of relationship between observer and observed

It is impossible to know what effect the researcher had on the tribunal process. Occasionally, members commented on our presence or note-taking, making it clear that they were conscious of our presence.

In defining the relationship of the observer to the observed, Gold (1958) proposes a four-fold typology ranging from complete observer, observer as participant, participant as observer through to complete participant. While this typology improves upon the previous dichotomous participant/non-participant observer roles, it fails to capture adequately the relationship that the researchers in this study had with the members being observed.

Atkinson and Hammersley (1998) state that the rhetoric of observation is egalitarian: observer and observed as inhabitants of a shared social and cultural field. The disjuncture between the researcher and the researched in this research context could not, however, have been more acute. The research had been funded by the Department of Health, and was therefore imbued with a sense of evaluation and judgement of those we were observing. In addition, access to the field of observation had to be negotiated at every hearing in a very explicit way; and we could not, even if we had wished, slip in and out of meetings undetected.

Consequently, although we were not in any sense participating in the decision-making, we were acutely aware that we had a very visible presence within the tribunal setting. In a small cramped room there are few places to hide. In addition, we were unable to cultivate the position of the 'marginal native' (Freilich, 1970). Our sole purpose was to observe and record the decision-makers: we could not pretend that our gaze was elsewhere or that we were involved in a collective endeavour of tribunal decision-making.

Access

Following the problems encountered at the beginning of the research, consent to observe the tribunals was negotiated in stages.

The regional chairman wrote to all tribunal presidents in each of the four regions. These letters described the study, and emphasised that observation of each tribunal was subject to the agreement of the president and the patient. Members were encouraged to participate other than in exceptional circumstances.

Three tribunal presidents declined to take part in the study.

Observations took place in two-week blocks, with observations in each region being completed before observations started in another. Tribunal office staff collated information on all the section 2 and section 3 tribunals scheduled during the study period. This usually involved listing the tribunals, and their locations, taking place within the specified time frame. Any tribunal under the chairmanship of one of the non-participating tribunal presidents was excluded from the list. Researchers selected hearings in a chronological order over that period and tribunal office staff were given details of those to be observed.

Tribunal office staff then telephoned the relevant tribunal presidents to inform them that a tribunal over which they were presiding had been selected for observation. Presidents were again asked at this stage whether they had any objections to an observer being present at the pre-hearing meeting and the deliberation.

The procedure worked less well in those regions in which there were a number of cancellations[3]. A total of 21 tribunals, which were selected for observation, were cancelled shortly before the scheduled hearing. Reselection of tribunals to replace those cancelled had to take place at short notice; these were the occasions on which the researcher was most likely to have to negotiate directly with the tribunal president. Inevitably, this occurred more often with section 2 hearings than with section 3 hearings.

The mechanism for seeking the patient's consent to observe their tribunal varied across the regions. In all instances, the patient was asked in the presence of their legal representative prior to the hearing. Three patients were not represented. Where this occurred, the study was explained to the patient by the clerk. They were asked if they wished to participate and were assured that their decision would not affect the tribunal hearing or outcome in any way. At the beginning of all tribunals, after the introductions had been made, the tribunal president publicly checked that the patient was content for the researcher to be present at the tribunal.

Table 3.1 *Section of patients in observed tribunals*

Section of patient	Region 1	Region 2	Region 3	Region 4	Total
Section 2	6	2	8	2	18
Section 3	9	14	7	13	43

We were given full access to the reports during the hearing. The researchers also negotiated with the Department of Health for access to the reports held at the tribunal offices. This was important, as there was not always adequate time to record all the relevant background information from the reports and researchers did not retain any copies of information submitted to the tribunal.

Basis for recruitment to the sample

Apart from the issue of consent, the only externally imposed criterion on selection for inclusion was the section of the hearing. We wanted to over-sample section 3 hearings for a number of reasons (see Table 3.1). The implications of being detained under section 3 were very different from those of being detained under section 2 in terms of the length and nature of detention. In addition, section 3 hearings were by their very nature scheduled in a more planned and coordinated way. We believed that this would provide a better basis from which to analyse the decision-making process. In each region the ratio of section 2 to section 3 hearings was kept under constant review.

We found during the initial setting-up periods that tribunal members treated us with great courtesy and showed an interest in the study. However, as the hearings progressed, members appeared to forget or shut out our presence. There were three occasions on which researchers were asked to stop recording what was being said. In all three instances this occurred in the deliberation, and related to the anger and frustration being expressed by the tribunal members towards the care that a patient was receiving. When this happened the text was marked and notes were subsequently made from memory.

Ethical issues

Many of the ethical issues arising from non-participant observation did not apply in this study. Erikson identifies two major areas in which observational research can be unethical.

(i) It is unethical for a sociologist to deliberately misrepresent his identity for the purpose of entering a private domain to which he is not otherwise eligible.

(ii) It is unethical for a sociologist to deliberately misrepresent the character of the research in which he is engaged (Erikson, 1967, p. 373).

Throughout all our observations we were marked out as researchers. We could not misrepresent the nature of our research because gaining access had involved detailed negotiations about what we would be observing and for what purpose. This was reinforced through the process of gaining consent, which required all the key participants – tribunal members, patients and their legal representatives – to agree to our presence.

Interviews

We also carried out in-depth interviews with 24 tribunal members to examine their knowledge of, and beliefs about, the decision-making. Six members were interviewed in each of the four participating regions: two legal, two medical and two lay members (see Topic Guide, Appendix 3).

Piloting of interviews

The Topic Guide was developed and piloted in one region after observations had been completed. In both the pilot and the main stage of the data collection, the researchers who conducted the interviews were not involved in the main stage observation of tribunals. This was to ensure that discussion about individual cases did not take place. The purpose of the research was to elucidate the decision-making process, not to assess whether the right or wrong decision had been made. Each interview lasted between 30 and 90 minutes. With respondent's permission, interviews were tape recorded and transcribed.

Sample

In each region, the regional chairmen were asked to nominate individuals for interview. This sample was boosted by members selected at random by the researchers from tribunal member lists.

Analysis

The process of analysis was iterative, drawing on both interview and observational data to identify themes. The data enables a comprehensive analysis of what tribunal members say they do and what they actually do in practice when making decisions about the discharge of patients from section 2 and section 3 of the MHA 1983.

In practice the differences between section 2 and section 3 hearings in terms of the nature and volume of evidence presented to the tribunal did not substantially affect the way in which decision-making took place. Except where differences were observed, the analysis deals with the decision-making in section 2 and section 3 tribunals together.

Details of the tribunal sample

A total of 61 tribunals were observed in four regions of England.

Three patients refused researchers access to their tribunal. In addition, three tribunal members expressed reservations about the study and declined us access to their tribunals. Given this low level of refusal, and given that there were no major policy changes or events during the period of observation, we feel confident that the observed tribunals were broadly representative of tribunals taking place in all four regions at that time.

Patient characteristics

The majority of patients in the sample were aged between 16 and 35 (Table 3.2). There were slightly more men than women (Table 3.3) and approximately one quarter were from an ethnic minority (Table 3.4). The majority of the sample had had previous contact with mental health services and the principal MHA 1983 diagnostic classification was mental illness (mainly different forms of schizophrenia). All bar three were represented.

Of the 61 tribunals we observed, the majority were section 3 hearings (see Table 3.1).

Table 3.2 *Age of patients in observed tribunals*

Age of patient	Region 1	Region 2	Region 3	Region 4	Total
Less than 31 years	11	7	7	4	29
31–50 years	1	8	4	10	23
51+ years	3	1	4	1	9

Table 3.3 *Sex of patients in observed tribunals*

Sex of patient	Region 1	Region 2	Region 3	Region 4	Total
Male	8	9	8	10	35
Female	7	7	7	5	26

Table 3.4 *Ethnicity of patients in observed tribunals*

Ethnicity of patient	Region 1	Region 2	Region 3	Region 4	Total
White	10	12	9	15	46
Ethnic minority	5	4	6	-	15

A note about the presentation of data

In this report all data is anonymised. Wherever a patient's name was used in the tribunal, the researcher substituted 'patient'. We have retained this convention throughout the report. All observational material records the person who spoke and identifies the text spoken with a ➜. The legal member is referred to throughout the text as the president. This reflects the common practice. In the transcript quotes, for both the interviews and observational data, they are identified as 'Pres'. Throughout the report, the medical member is referred to as the medical member and the notation is 'MM'. The lay member is referred to as the lay member and the notation is 'LM'. The patient's legal representative is represented by the notation 'LR'. All observational material is quoted verbatim. On the rare occasions where not all the speech is reported, the missing text is denoted by '...'. Judgements pertaining to the length and selection of reported passages are those of the author and are guided by the need for accuracy and to avoid misrepresentation.

Notes

1 See for example, Hammersley and Atkinson, 1983; Hammersley, 1989; Silverman, 1993.

2 Based at London School of Economics, London.

3 Tribunals get cancelled for a number of reasons. However, according to the tribunal offices it is most commonly due to the discharge of the patient by the RMO prior to the tribunal taking place. It is impossible to know without detailed research what proportion of discharges by RMOs are precipitated by the patient's application to a tribunal and what proportion arise, coincidentally, from a routine consideration of the patient's progress. It is clear that in some cases the RMO is on the point of discharging the patient at the point the tribunal convenes. In these circumstances when a tribunal discharges the patient it is often only anticipating the discharge by a few days (Wood, 1993).

4

Roles of Members

This chapter explores the roles of members in theory and in practice. It also examines the approach adopted by all members to the reports presented to the tribunal. Interview data and observational data are drawn on to highlight some of the issues inherent in their roles. Subsequent chapters examine the way in which members' roles differed in the three stages of the tribunal.

Each tribunal panel has three members – a legal member, who sits as the president or chair of the tribunal, a medical member, and a lay member. In addition, a tribunal clerk is responsible for setting up the hearing and, in our observations, was usually present. The clerk ensures the smooth running of the tribunal – organising the room in which the hearing takes place, providing the correct number of copies of background papers and reports, gathering the witnesses and the patient together, and organising refreshments for the members. The role of the clerk will be discussed in subsequent chapters but, essentially, clerks play no formal part in the tribunals' decision-making[1].

Role descriptions

The 'official' role descriptions of tribunal members are set out in a *Guide for Members* (1996b). This summarises and interprets the code of procedure embodied in the Rules (SI 1983 No. 942). Training is now provided for members but, at the time of the study, access to the course was not guaranteed before new members started. It was far more common for new members to have been active for at least a year before they received any formal training. For the long-standing tribunal members and the majority of the ones we observed, 'Sitting next to Nellie' had been the only training on offer to them: as one lay member described it: 'You watch three tribunals and then you do it. I was appalled at the quality of some of the discussion which I was made to observe' (LM 05).

All of the interviewed tribunal members felt strongly about training. They generally felt that there should be regular training sessions addressing issues of both law and process. None of the members made use of the hearings as training opportunities, as described by Sir John Wood in his foreword at the beginning of the *Guide for Members* (1996b):

What has tended to be somewhat neglected is the old-fashioned notion that the best training is actually performing the function itself. This is still a truism, but is only an effective one if the members of each tribunal use sittings constructively and find a little time when the case is over to discuss the problems they encountered and put them in to the wider context of their experience. In that way each member builds a valuable and essential expertise.

Members learned their roles through observation of others and through the experience of 'being' a tribunal member. The *Guide for Members* highlights the range of activities specified for each member; these are fully reproduced in Appendix 4 and summarised below.

The role of the tribunal president

The president's specific responsibility for directing the proceedings during the hearing is intended to make sure that the applicant receives a fair hearing. This includes making sure that the patient (or their legal representative) has an opportunity to put their case, to hear all the evidence against them, and to refute allegations. The legal member, as president, is also responsible for making sure that the members deliberate together after the hearing, and for writing the reasons for the tribunal's decision, taking into account contributions from the other members.

The role of the medical member

The medical member, normally a consultant (or retired consultant) psychiatrist, has responsibility for examining the applicant to form their own opinion of the patient's mental condition. The examination normally takes place a day or more before the hearing. The Rules state:

At any time before the hearing of application, the medical member, or where the tribunal includes more than one, at least one of them shall examine the patient and take such other steps as he considers necessary to form an opinion of the patient's mental condition; and for this purpose the patient may be seen in private and all his medical records may be examined by the medical member, who may take such notes and copies of them as he may require, for use in connection with the application [and in the case of a patient subject to after-care under supervision this rule shall also apply to such other records relating to any after-care services provided under section 117 of the Act]. (SI 1983 No. 942, Rule 11)

When the members meet in the pre-hearing meeting, the medical member may be asked to report on this examination. The *Guide for Members* (1996b) states that it is usually inappropriate for the medical member to give an opinion of the patient's mental condition at this stage (1996b, p. 49).

The role of the lay member

The lay member is seen as 'providing a balance as a representative of the community outside the legal and medical professions' (Mental Health Review Tribunals for England and Wales, 1996). The lay member is, however, expected to have experience or knowledge of the health and social service systems, sometimes with a background in mental health. Their responsibilities at the hearing are less defined than those of the other members, and involve questioning witnesses during the hearing. In the *Guide*, the only specific task suggested for the lay member is to lead the questioning of the social worker 'if this has been agreed beforehand with the other members of the tribunal' (1996, p. 50). The *Guide* does not specify on what the lay member should question the social worker. The *Guide* emphasises that the lay member is entitled to an equal voice in reaching a decision.

So what happens in practice?

The tribunal president

The legal member is the tribunal president and has the widest range of responsibilities, which fall into two categories: chairing the hearing, and providing legal expertise.

Chairing the hearing

In our observations, we found that all presidents introduced the other tribunal members to the patient, they stressed the independence of the tribunal from the hospital, and ensured that the legal representative was given an opportunity to question each witness. There was, however, a great deal of variation at every stage of the tribunal in the way that the president controlled the proceedings. This variation included: the information discussed and revealed in the pre-hearing meeting; the ordering of witnesses; and the management of the deliberation. The differences in approach, evident in the interview material, will be explored in more detail in the following chapters.

All the presidents emphasised the importance of establishing a fair hearing in which all participants had an opportunity to contribute:

> *I'm clear that the role of the Chair is to make sure there is a fair and proper hearing – that's one of the things I'm clear about. To make sure, as far as possible, the three Members of the Tribunal have an equal say on what goes on in an equal role. But also to make absolutely sure that the patient has had every opportunity either through a representative or in person to say what they want to say or to question any of the witnesses or to challenge any of the material the Tribunal has before it.* (Pres 07)

There was less consensus on the ordering of evidence, with some presidents believing that the patient's evidence should come first and some believing that the RMO's evidence should be taken first. The ordering of evidence is explored more fully in Chapter 6.

> *The practice that tends to evolve … is that there's a sort of expectation on the psychiatrist's part that he will go first when he's questioning the RMO and likewise the lay members tend to assume that they'll get the first crack at the social worker. I think that's a very, it may be symbolic, but it's a very simplistic approach to what the real roles are.* (Pres 07)

Legal expertise

As the legal expert on the panel, tribunal presidents are responsible for advising the other members on any points of law, in particular the application of the statutory criteria for discharge. In interpreting the law, they have a contribution to make both at the beginning of the tribunal in the pre-hearing meeting and during deliberation. In practice, presidents provided only limited advice and guidance on the application of the law.

The president is also required to keep a record[2] of the main statements during the proceedings. If a patient were then to seek judicial review, these notes would be disclosable as evidence.

> *I mean my role as chairman is to take a good note of the evidence and obviously if you're making good note of evidence you can't necessarily be asking lots of questions as well, so I try and leave the question asking very much to the wing members and obviously mop up afterwards if there are any questions that I think we haven't asked that we need to have done, or if there are further lines of enquiry to pursue. But I see my role very much as making sure we've got a note of what's being said and understanding all that's going on and really letting them do the bulk of the question asking. That's the format, the way it tends to go.* (Pres 14)

This president was unusual in placing so much emphasis on note-taking. Other presidents recognised the problems of taking good contemporaneous notes, listening to the information being provided, assimilating it and identifying gaps in the information elicited. In practice there also appeared to be a number of different approaches to note-taking. We observed the majority of presidents selectively recording information, and a minority recording little or nothing. During the deliberation, one president drew attention to his note-taking, stating:

> *Pres ➜ I stopped taking notes. She didn't seem to be answering the questions.* (RC03)

There was only one occasion (RB16) during a deliberation when the president used his notes to check what a patient had actually said.

All presidents took responsibility for the writing of the decision, on the grounds that this was a clearly defined legal responsibility.

The medical member

The medical member has the clearest and most contentious role of the tribunal members. As the *Guide for Members* states, the medical member:

> *must appreciate that he performs a dual role at the tribunal as a fact finder and as a decision-maker.* [1996b, p. 49]

The medical member sees the applicant before the hearing. This is one of the key elements of the medical member's role and means that they often bring substantial new information to the tribunal. As one said:

> *I arrive at a tribunal already familiar with the case and usually I'm more familiar with the case than the RMO.* (MM 03)

Due to staffing problems in the hospital there were a few instances in which the patient attending a tribunal had been cared for by a series of locum psychiatrists. In the tribunal hearing both the locum RMO and the patient acknowledged the lack of continuous care as a problem in arriving at an accurate picture of the patient's current condition. However, it was usual for the tribunal medical members to spend an hour or more with each patient on the day before the tribunal, during which time they were able to form an opinion of the patient's mental state. The medical members we interviewed recognised that this contact with the patient made their tribunal role distinctive and influential.

Many critics of the tribunal system see the dual role of the medical member as one of the fundamental flaws in tribunal decision-making (Peay, 1989; Richardson, 1999). The medical member provides an 'independent' assessment of the patient's mental state through an examination of the patient prior to the hearing. In undertaking this examination, the medical member is also directed to take such steps as he considers necessary to form an opinion of the patient's mental condition. These steps should include reference to hospital documentation and discussions with hospital staff:

> *I try to get straight at the case notes when I visit. And brief myself more completely. For two reasons – because I think the case notes often contain the raw material from which the report was derived, and may therefore actually be more relevant. And secondly because the reports are often not contemporaneous. With the section 2s you're lucky to have a report when you do the preliminary examination. With the section 3s the position is opposite, that the report may have been made several weeks before and there may have been a delay in the tribunal. So you need actually to find out what's been happening in that period, which as I say, sometimes may be several weeks, to see whether the situation is still the same. And it sometimes isn't. I mean sometimes the*

patient has actually improved and they've actually been to some residential accommodation in the community, and they're thinking it over. So the situation will often have moved forward quite considerably. Now that will probably come out when the RMO and the social worker are interviewed, but I think it's important that I should if possible be up-to-date before I join them. (MM 22)

However, because of their dual role as fact finders and decision-makers, the way in which this new information is handled is quite heavily prescribed. The member's *Guide* states that – first, it is usually inappropriate for the medical member to give an opinion of the patient's mental condition in the pre-hearing meeting; and, second, it is essential that the medical member's 'opinion of the patient's mental condition, if it differs significantly from that of the RMO, should be made known to everyone present in the course of his questioning' (*Guide for Members*, 1996b, p. 49). There would be a breach of a fundamental principle of natural justice if members of the tribunal were in possession of evidence known only to themselves. While there are some protocols about how the medical member reports back to the other tribunal members in the pre-hearing meeting, it is very much up to the president to determine how this is done.

Well the medical member has an obvious role because they've had to have seen the patient in advance, so they've had to have looked into the whole question of what the mental illness is and formed a view as to whether they agree or not with the diagnosis and treatment so that they can advise us. If they have a contrary view we obviously have to air that in the hearing. (Pres 14)

Jones (1996), the authoritative tribunal *Mental Health Act Manual*, and Eldergill (1998, p. 805) suggest that the medical member is meant to confine the pre-hearing report to factual matters, reserving opinion until after the evidence has been taken. The reasoning behind this is clear – the tribunal as a whole is meant to determine the issues relating to the patient's mental condition in the light of the member's own experience and examination of the patient during the hearing (Jones, 1996, p. 473).

The extent to which medical members conveyed an impression, or sometimes overtly expressed their opinion, about whether the patient should be discharged was largely negotiated and controlled by the president. However, as one president pointed out, opinions can sometimes come in the guise of facts:

Most of them will tell you the facts, a lot of which is already in the papers without giving an opinion, but they will state an opinion as a fact. (Pres 07)

Medical members recognised that, through their examination of the patient, they had frequently formed an opinion one way or another about the patient and their suitability for discharge, which they were then required, somehow, to suspend:

Of course one does form an opinion – I always drive away from them thinking either, they haven't got a chance of getting off – or thinking, 'I can't under-

> *stand why that person's on a section, I mean the RMOs going to have to come up with some startling evidence to persuade us that they should remain on section'. Or a third possibility, which is the one I enjoy most, is coming away thinking 'I don't know'. I certainly don't share it with the panel beforehand. It would prejudice the tribunal obviously because they do tend to set a lot of store on our opinion.* (MM 03)

Our interviews showed that there is currently some uncertainty among members about the type of information that it was acceptable to hear without prejudicing the hearing. Although the factual basis of medical opinion may be open to challenge by cross-examination and by evidence, the medical member's examination of the patient is considered to be part of the deliberative process and not part of the evidence.

All medical members recognised there was a danger that patients saw the medical member of the tribunal as 'on their side'.

> *I also feel it's important to say 'We'll be meeting again tomorrow or this afternoon, the other two members will be a lawyer and an ordinary person, the lawyer will be in charge ... and we'll ask some of the same things that we've asked you know, but there may be other things' and I say it's meant to be informal, it's not meant to be a court of law so don't be intimidated and, you know, if you feel uncomfortable your nurse will be with you probably ... Obviously this is a big occasion for them and I'm not sure, you're never sure to what extent they've been informed about it.* (MM 22)

> *The tribunal doctor is almost a double agent because in a way you make friends with them and they see you on the other side of the table and they think ah well, he's on my side and even though I've told them quite clearly that I'm not on anybody's side, they talk quite freely and that's not necessarily to their advantage, as far as their situation is concerned.* (MM 10)

The presidents and lay members we interviewed were cautious in their assessment of how independent a medical member could be. They often pointed out that the medical member had been a practising psychiatrist and, as such, was likely to hold similar views about treatment in the NHS as the RMOs who were appearing as witnesses arguing in favour of the patient's continued detention. In addition, it was possible that the medical member would know some of the RMOs personally. In one tribunal the following exchanges were recorded:

> *MM ➜ Will you stop the [legal] rep having a go at the SHO?*
> *Pres ➜ No, I can't do that if it's reasonable questioning.*
> *MM ➜ But she is inexperienced.*
> *Pres ➜ We can't make allowances for the hospital not being able to supply someone more experienced.* (RD14)

One president explained the relationship between medical members and RMOs in terms of 'the enormous depth of professional courtesy between the doctors'. When asked how this was manifest, the president said that it was demonstrated in a 'marked reluctance to contradict each other' with medical members preferring to ask 'penetrating questions about the actual practice in that particular hospital' (Pres 07).

> *One tries to actually have a word with the RMO at some point before the meeting if possible, but it's not always, you know, possible to do that. And I certainly try to talk to one of the nursing staff who knows the patient well. Because I feel that they are much closer, and they're often not ... the major witness at the actual tribunal, although they may be the people in many instances who give you a very much ... more sensitive feel about what's happening.* (MM 22)

> *Whereas when I go and see a section 2, I will be provided with notes which may or may not be good and I may find that they have already typed a report, that's if I do it on the day of the tribunal. I mean, I think it's undesirable to do the examination on the day of the tribunal but timewise, and particularly if you have a lot of travelling to do, it can be quite difficult to fit in, even with the relative amounts of flexibility time that I have now that I'm not actually an NHS consultant.* (MM 04)

There was substantial variation in the volume of information provided by medical members for the other members, and in the extent to which they conveyed an impression, or overtly expressed their opinion, about whether the patient should be discharged.

Medical members are also, more than the other two members, the 'expert' on the panel because their formal diagnostic skills give them the unique ability to challenge the RMO, who is usually the major obstacle to the patient's discharge. Several members we interviewed said they thought the medical member's role was the most important on the tribunal.

The lay member

The medical members and presidents considered themselves, and each other, to have clearly identified roles. However, the majority of presidents interviewed said they thought it important to allocate at least one responsibility, or area of expertise, to the lay member to make them feel included:

> *I think the lay member can actually feel quite left out because they feel everybody has asked all the questions before they've had a chance.* (Pres 20)

> *The lay member ... is often sort of shoved aside – they need a specific role so they're sort of given certain tasks in advance.* (Pres 01)

There was a sense in which lay members were, therefore, seen as passive, as requiring other tribunal members to stake out a claim for their right to be there. And yet, as a group, they reflect a range of professional interests – psychiatric nurses, mental health social workers and magistrates.

The legal and medical members appeared fairly confident of the role expected of them. However, in the interviews lay members talked about feeling side-lined and uneasy:

> *Sometimes there are burning questions within me as a lay person which I won't really ask ... no-one has told me what the boundaries are.* (LM 24)

> *With two professionals there, it was a question of what do I do, where do I fit in?* (LM 23)

Although lay members sometimes appeared to feel uncertain at the tribunal, and spoke significantly less than the other two members in all stages of the tribunal, in the interviews they were quick to note the importance of their role and had a strong sense of role identity. They described this as bringing an independent, impartial view, and a wider experience of the world to bear on the tribunal. They also emphasised their ability not only to understand the 'outside world', but also to communicate with the patient:

> *And I've come across at least one lay member who I thought very sensibly regarded part of her role as keeping the psychiatrists apart, stopping them conspiring together and stitching the whole thing up. So I think if a lay person views themselves as having that sort of role and there's evidence that the psychiatrists are getting together in a little professional corner I think that should be encouraged, you know, that lay members should wade in.* (Pres 07)

Lay members suffer because their exact contribution is not made explicit and because their allocated role relates to the social elements of community care. The relevance of these social circumstances to the statutory criteria for discharge is not clearly defined in the MHA (1983). However, they are central to how a patient might manage once a decision to discharge has been taken. In the observed tribunals the area most consistently served by poor information related to the family, social, employment and daily living circumstances of the patient in the community.

Reading of the reports

Reports are submitted to the tribunal from the patient's RMO and from the patient's social worker. The content of the reports and the extent to which they reflected the patient's condition varied enormously in the observed tribunals. Section 2 reports were usually shorter and contained the most up-to-date information. Section 3 reports varied in length, accuracy and in the extent to which they described the patient's current mental state.

The RMO's report

The RMO's report is usually taken to represent the views of the responsible authority on the suitability of the patient for discharge. The content of the RMO's report provided is covered by Rule 6, Schedule Part A and Part B (1) of SI 1983 No. 942. The information to be provided includes:

(1) Full name of patient.
(2) Age of patient.
(3) Date of admission to hospital in which patient is currently detained.
(4) Where the patient is being treated in a nursing home under contractual arrangements with a health authority, the name of that authority.
(5) Details of the original authority for the detention or guardianship of the patient, including the Act of Parliament and the section of the Act by reference to which detention was authorised and details of any subsequent renewal of or change in the authority for detention.
(6) The form of mental disorder from which the patient is recorded as suffering in the authority for detention (including amendments, if any, under section 16 or 72 (5) of the Act, but excluding cases within section 5 of the Criminal Procedure (Insanity) Act 1964).
(7) The name of the responsible medical officer and the period which the patient has spent under the care of that officer.
(8) Where another registered medical practitioner is or has recently been largely concerned in the treatment of the patient, the name of that practitioner and the period which the patient has spent under his care.
(9) The dates of all previous tribunal hearings in relation to the patient, the decisions reached at such hearings and the reasons given. (In restricted patient cases this requirement does not relate to decisions before 30 September 1983).
(10) Details of any proceedings in the Court of Protection and of any receivership order made in respect of the patient.
(11) The name and address of the patient's nearest relative or of any other person who is exercising that function.
(12) The name and address of any other person who takes a close interest in the patient.
(13) Details of any leave of absence granted to the patient during the previous two years, including the duration of such leave and particulars of the arrangements made for the patient's residence while on leave.

The social circumstances report

The content of the social circumstances report is covered under Part VII, Part B of the schedule to SI 1983 No. 942. It requires details of:

(a) The patient's home and family circumstances, including the attitude of the patient's nearest relative or the person so acting;

(b) Opportunities for employment or occupation and the housing facilities which would be available to the patient if discharged;
(c) The availability of community support and relevant medical facilities;
(d) The financial circumstances of the patient.

In addition, the report should include the views of the authority on the 'suitability of the patient for discharge and any other observations which the authority wishes to make' (SI 1983 No. 942).

The case for continued detention, as first presented to the tribunal, is portrayed through reports submitted by the responsible authority and the local authority. By definition, these reports almost exclusively define the case for the patient's detention. The patient's view is not at this stage represented in a report to the tribunal. The early presentation of the case to the tribunal through the reports is therefore one that argues strongly or otherwise for the patient's detention.

The reports for a section 2 hearing, unlike a section 3 hearing, are not circulated in advance. In section 2 cases, the date for the hearing is fixed upon receipt of an application. Given that patients may apply for a tribunal within 14 days of being admitted, beginning with the day on which they were admitted, and given that the order for assessment enables a patient to be detained for 28 days only, there is insufficient time for reports to be written and circulated prior to the hearing. The reports for a section 2 hearing are therefore tabled on the day.

Both types of report are meant to address the specific legal criteria for discharge.

The standard of medical and social reports submitted to tribunals varied enormously. The sources of variation included the date when reports were written, the content, and the structure of the information. In a small minority of cases, the RMO reports were out of date by as much as a couple of months by the time of the hearing. In the observed tribunals, all members had received section 3 reports in advance of the hearing and on a small number of occasions the RMOs had furnished the tribunal with written updates on the day of the tribunal:

> *The reason why we don't get reports from certain hospitals is that the RMOs in certain hospitals either don't produce reports at all … or if they do produce them they produce them on the hoof at the last moment. Or even on the hoof in the tribunal itself, please don't get the impression this is every time.* (MM 21)

The members' *Guide* (p. 7) identifies the advantages to be gained from reading the reports in advance:

(1) It might transpire that the member has had a previous contact with the patient which excludes him from sitting on a particular case (SI 1983 No. 942, Rule 8(2)c).
(2) It could promote an effective hearing.
(3) It might lessen the possibility of the need for an adjournment if it is discovered for example that further information is required.

The interview data revealed that all members looked at the papers in advance. However, all commented on the frequency with which hearings were cancelled and their consequent reluctance to invest too much time in advance of the hearing in reading the reports and 'marking them up'.

Members approached report reading in broadly similar ways. Major differences arose in identification of salient points:

The envelope comes through the door, I read them – I skim read them almost as soon as they come through the door, and that, to be honest, is mainly to check whether there's any prospect of there being a conflict because obviously I have represented quite a lot of patients in the past so I need just to double-check that it's not someone who I suddenly remember from the dim and distant past. It's actually never happened because I do quite a careful check when I get booked in for a tribunal. So I skim read it then and then I'm afraid I put them away until two or three days before, because so many patients are discharged it's not worth looking at them until nearer the time. And then two or three days before, I will get them out and read them through really quite carefully and probably prepare a list of questions that I think need to be asked. I also, I mean I do a check about a couple of weeks before to ensure that I've got all the reports, so if we're short of a report then I'll tend to chase the tribunal offices to find out what's happening. (Pres 08)

I certainly don't write it down or anything like that but I think 'Ah yes well I need to know this and that and the other' because it's not clear from the report. So you're starting already to sort of assimilate the evidence which you feel that you need to make sure is given at the tribunal. (Pres 20)

Tribunal presidents were reading the reports to check that all the pages were there, check particular aspects of the legislation that might become important, and generally identify issues that might need to be addressed, usually by the medical member.

Like the tribunal presidents, lay members also stated that they read the papers in advance in order to identify issues pertinent to their questioning of the patient and other witnesses:

Notes would be made on the type of questions I might be asking. But I prefer to do that, to be sort of prepared before I go. (LM 24)

Well I highlight things that jump out of the page so I read them first of all with an idea of getting a feel. And I do actually write down things that I'm curious about and wish to know the answers to; supposing they are discharged, how they would manage? and all those sort of things. I suppose I would put them under headings of manageability of symptoms, medication, money, relationships, accepting care, all those. Sometimes I make more notes than others do really, it very much depends. (LM 11)

> *What I do actually is go right the way through the reports and underline what I think are the points that need raising within the tribunal itself ... I highlight those and much of the background you can hold but I think the important points, you must have there so that as you're going through questions with the social workers, you can quickly glance and make sure that not one of those points is missed, and I think that's important.* (LM 12)

Medical members had more diverse approaches to report reading, reflecting their role and expertise. The majority of medical members felt that the medical reports provided a useful synthesis of what could otherwise be a large body of complex material:

> *I read them the day before I make the preliminary examination. I do not read them the moment they arrive, because there's no point in doing that, I read them and then I make up my own mind, but it means that when I see the patient there's a whole lot of information that I don't need to ask the patient.* (MM 04)

In a minority of cases medical members did not read the reports in advance or view them as helpful:

> *I don't read them in advance ... I must admit I don't take a lot of notice of the report before I see the patient because I try to approach the fact-finding exercise if you like without prejudice.* (MM 03)

Although all members recognised in the interviews that the reports could contain factual inaccuracies, these were only likely to be uncovered in the hearing if specifically challenged by the patient or legal representative.

Summary

The tribunal members participating in this study had learned their roles through reading, observation and practice. Although a formal training programme had been introduced, none of the tribunal members in this study had received the training prior to sitting as a tribunal member. It is not therefore surprising that there was huge variation in the way members performed their roles. The greatest variation being observed among the tribunal presidents and medical members. Lay members played a less substantial role in the proceedings and it was therefore not possible to discern much variation.

The tribunal presidents varied in the extent to which they controlled each stage of the proceedings and applied their legal expertise. The medical member as a fact-finder and a decision-maker plays a more complex role in tribunals. It is in relation to their examination of the patient prior to the tribunal and the oral report given to the other tribunal members in the pre-hearing meeting that greatest variation arises. These elements will be discussed in more detail in relation to the stage of the tribunal proceedings in which they occur.

Notes

1 Since this research was carried out, a shortage of clerks has resulted in the majority of hearings being unclerked (Department of Health, 2002a). The majority of tribunals in this study had a clerk in attendance.

2 In the *Tribunal News Sheet* (15 June 1995) Christie, Regional Chairman of North Thames, writes about his experience of surrendering his notebook for evidential purposes in a Judicial Review. He urges all legal members to keep a chronological record of events throughout the hearing and suggests that the outdoor clerk for the tribunal on the day should keep a backup record, notwithstanding the lack of the clerk's legal qualification.

5

The Pre-hearing Meeting

The pre-hearing meeting takes place half an hour before the beginning of the tribunal hearing. Much of what has been written by policy-makers about this meeting relates to the examination of the patient by the medical member. Less often discussed is the contribution made by this meeting to the process of decision-making.

In this chapter we analyse the views of the members on the nature and purpose of the pre-hearing meeting and identify the role of this meeting in the decision-making process.

Nature and purpose of the pre-hearing meeting

Members held differing views about the nature and purpose of the pre-hearing meeting. The majority felt that the time set aside for the pre-hearing meeting allowed them to relax and catch up with other members' news, thus enhancing the informality of the tribunal hearing:

> *I think very often people have driven a long way and probably driven a long way under quite busy traffic conditions ... I think it gives people a chance to sit down, have a cup of coffee and relax. And that's good because I think that* [it] *is really important that people are relaxed and give a relaxed approach to the people who are coming in before the tribunal.* (Pres 20)

> *Very often it's a waste of time ... I wouldn't say it's not used fruitfully, you've got the papers, you've got your other colleagues ... And so you're meeting old friends again in a sense, so that time isn't wasted.* (LM 23)

In our observations, there was indeed an emphasis on catching up with or getting to know other members. Good relationships were viewed as the cement within which good decisions could be cast:

> *I think quite honestly it's a good idea for tribunal members to get to know each other and have a feeling for each other. A rapport before you start.* (Pres 13)

It's get the papers together, sit down, go to the loo, have a cup of coffee, I mean, generally speaking it's very cynical in some ways, one knows the tribunal members and you know one gets on well with them and it all sorts itself out during the course of the tribunal. (MM 06)

In all cases, half an hour was set aside before the beginning of the tribunal to discuss the case. However, the use of this time varied. Across all tribunals, in all participating regions, the average time spent discussing the case in the pre-hearing meetings was 25 minutes, with actual times ranging from 5 minutes to one hour. Two-thirds of these preliminary discussions took 30 minutes or less; and in one fifth of all tribunals the pre-hearing meeting was over in 10 minutes or less.

It's a short exchange of views. Sometimes you could do it in five minutes; sometimes it does take longer. (MM 15)

And I look on the pre-hearing meeting as just a procedure which will assist me to ask the right questions at the tribunal, so that I understand what it's all about. I mean it's called an 'assessment' but you can't actually take a view until you hear what the hospital doctor says and the Social Worker. (MM 10)

Some of the time not spent discussing the case was spent reading reports. This was always true for section 2 hearings where reports were tabled on the day. The time spent reading reports ranged from 5 to 15 minutes.

All members recognised the opportunity afforded by the pre-hearing meeting to clarify any uncertainties about issues or roles in advance of the hearing and to crystallise the key issues arising from reports:

My feeling is that what we actually want is a good discussion. If we do this at the start, before the meeting – identify what we are actually looking for, where are we going to go, what is this case about, what are the issues raised by this case, how are we going to encapsulate those, what are the actual decisions we're going to need to make – we're actually focused on the way through. (Pres 02)

And if there's something wrong with the report sometimes, the reports are obviously defective – just haven't given enough detail about anything, you can discuss as a group what you're going to do about this; are you going to ask for an adjournment, are you going to cope with the reports that you've got and actually just question the people more, and you learn who's coming and if there's a problem about the patient being represented or if they're going to bring ten relatives in, are you going to let all the relatives speak or not, those sorts of procedural issues. (LM 05)

Well, I think it's very valuable actually because there are points that are helpful to discuss amongst yourselves, what should be brought out in the hearing, you may decide which member is going to deal with a particular point. (Pres 13)

We all read the papers, if we haven't already read them before we start ... and if it's a section 2, we all sit quietly and read the papers. Then I always say 'Well if everybody's read the papers?', 'Yes', 'Right Dr Jones when did you see the patient?' 'This morning' or 'yesterday afternoon' right, 'How did you find the patient?' right 'We see that he's on this medication – is that a high dose or a low dose because we've read it in the papers?'... But we sometimes have things that we might particularly pinpoint as being important at that stage. And then we always conclude by saying 'but anyway we've got to wait and see how it goes', because often it changes as it goes along, as you would expect. So that's the way we use that half-hour. (Pres 19)

Conduct of the pre-hearing meeting

Although members stated in the interviews that they had a clear approach to the information contained in the reports – identifying issues, highlighting discrepancies, and isolating gaps in the information – this was not evident in the pre-hearing meeting discussions. In this section of the report we examine how members' views on the conduct of the pre-hearing meeting elicited through interview differed from the behaviour observed in the pre-hearing meetings.

The president's role, as chair of the hearing, includes organising the proceedings and making sure that they are conducted in a fair and judicial manner. As the legal expert on the panel, they are responsible for advising the other members on any points of law, in particular on the application of the statutory criteria for discharge. 'Running' the hearing was the term most often used to describe the role of the president and this was the role the presidents perceived themselves to be carrying out.

It was generally considered that 'running' the tribunal involved creating a fair and judicial process and imposing a structure on all aspects of the hearing, most notably by teasing out the issues to be addressed in the hearing and allocating specific tasks to the other members of the tribunal and ordering the witnesses. In the majority of the interviews members reported that this was their impression of what did happen in tribunals.

I think generally there is a pattern established and ... they clarify in the preview that this is how they will proceed and I find that personally quite helpful. (LM 18)

In the observed tribunals, however, the president rarely discussed with the other members the order in which evidence would be taken. Each region adopted a consistent approach to whether the patient gave evidence first or last, but the practice varied across the regions. It was assumed that all members were familiar with the particular practices of that region.

Pres ➜ *(*to medical member and lay member*) I'll follow the normal pattern of questioning.* (RA06)

On the rare occasions in which discussions about the ordering of evidence took place, they arose from a desire to depart from the customary practice in that region and were usually instigated by concerns on the part of the medical member about the patient's ability or otherwise to sit through evidence provided by other people.

Allocation of roles

In the interviews the medical members and lay members expected the president to direct or at least help to determine each member's area of questioning. However, in only about one third of tribunals did presidents actively allocate particular roles. This usually involved confirmation that the medical member would address some of the issues raised in the preliminary discussion or would question the RMO and that the lay member might address some of the social issues:

> *Pres* ➜ (addressing the medical member) *Have you any thoughts on that? Perhaps you could pursue it in the hearing.* (RA04)
> *Pres* ➜ (addressing the medical member) *Could you take plans for treatment and* (turning to lay member) *could you take home leave?* (RC11)
> *Pres* ➜ (to the medical member) *You lean on the RMO and* (turning to the lay member) *you can explore the issue of the group home.* (RC09)

Lay members in particular felt that being allocated a task helped to legitimise their role:

> *I've found it helpful when the chairman/president actually gives you a task. If he says 'I'll leave that to you to ask', in other words giving you a job to do, whereas the medical members definitely have a job to do.* (LM 11)

In a few tribunals, the medical member prompted the president in to directing the management of the evidence:

> *MM* ➜ (turning to the tribunal president) *How do you want to play it?* (RD15)

In the majority of tribunals where roles were allocated, there was also some direction from the president concerning questions about the statutory criteria for discharge. These were mainly allocated to the medical member as part of questioning of the RMO. Where there was no explicit direction by the president about how the statutory criteria for discharge were to be explored, one of two approaches were adopted: either the president would ask them of the RMO at the beginning of the tribunal, after the introductions; or the medical member would ask them at the beginning of his questioning of the RMO. In the absence of discussion, the medical member appeared to pick up the president's cue – if the questions had not been asked, then the medical member asked them.

We are a working team, oh the great thing about the tribunal, I think and tribunal members is to know them fairly well and we have a circulating sort of circus shall we say in which we meet, you know, frequently and we are on the same wave length. We know what we think about it all and therefore we're not liable to disagree. People know my views on things and I know their views on things. However, sometimes you meet new people, completely new. (MM 06)

The fluency with which members assumed their roles was to some extent a function of their knowledge of custom and practice in that particular region and of the president. It was not evident, however, from the observed tribunals how new members learned about local custom and practice.

Pre-hearing discussions

Where discussions did take place in the pre-hearing meeting there were three main themes: i) medical and treatment issues; ii) legal and procedural issues; iii) social issues.

(i) Medical and treatment issues

The medical member examination – an informed opinion

The medical member has a duty to examine the patient prior to the hearing and form an opinion. The medical member's assessment can be as comprehensive and wide-ranging as they have time for. It is in the opinion forming that the independent expert view is meant to be brought to bear within the tribunal. How this expert view is managed within the tribunal is important. In this study there was considerable variation.

It was generally recognised that it was the president's responsibility to manage and control the information revealed in the pre-hearing meeting:

There's a big debate at the moment about how much the medical members should tell you about the previous discussions and I actually try and restrict that – I want to know whether there are any things they disagree with very strongly in the reports we've seen or any, you know, particular concerns such as, the patient won't be able to communicate or will have difficulty sitting and may want to give his evidence first – those sort of practical issues. And then if there's anything that's been thrown up in a report, sort of medical points or occasionally they may talk about a specific placement in the community and I'll ask the lay member if they know anything about it – quite often they may do, so we may discuss that. But I don't like the idea that you sit around beforehand and decide what the likely outcome is going to be. (Pres 08)

A few tribunal members demonstrated a surprising lack of awareness of the purpose of restricting the medical member's oral report and of the potential for this report to jeopardise a fair hearing:

> *Something I wasn't aware of until very recently is that the guidelines issued to doctors in fact tell doctors* not *to give an opinion prior to the hearing of the evidence.* (Pres 07)

> *I'm not sure what the purpose of such restrictions are. I can see that there's a question about whether you're prejudicing the other two members. I think we're somewhat more robust than that, that we're not so easily prejudiced.* (LM 05)

All members emphasised the importance of the medical member's view. 'Useful' 'important' and 'valuable' were the adjectives most often used in the interviews to describe the medical member's input:

> *I think it's useful to know what the medical member of the tribunal has found out about the patient and certainly from the point of view of bringing us up-to-date on what the situation is. And in particular, whether there are any very recent episodes of which we need to be aware.* (Pres 20)

> *The medical member is very important because obviously they're able to have an informed opinion of what the patient's current mental state is and that's obviously important both in section 2s and section 3s, in particular the section 3s where you have an old medical report very often and he can bring the tribunal up-to-date on what has happened. I also think that it's useful because the medical member has had the chance to read through the nursing notes and find out a lot about the patient's management on the ward which of course can also be very, very important. Sometimes, and this I admit came as a surprise when I first actually suddenly realised the RMOs probably only see the patient once during the admission and so on.* (Pres 20)

The value of the medical member's examination of the patients and subsequent oral report lay in its up-to-date nature and in the way in which it directed attention to aspects of the patient's condition:

> *Our medical member having seen the patient can often give us valuable information. They shouldn't prejudice us, but they can often give us very valuable information before we see the patient, and we look back and it might mean we don't put our foot in it. I mean it might be a patient who has just separated from their husband or something like this. Whereas if we know we can be a bit careful, you know if they're really upset about something, it's quite helpful to know before.* (LM 17)

> *I think it is important, particularly that the medical member is able to say his view, because he or she has already seen that person and they can say, without*

> *passing judgement whether that person should be discharged or not. They are able to say that in their view the patient is still recovering from illness, anything positive or negative and that is useful to know from our members' point of view.* (LM 18)

Members identified the pre-hearing meeting as the first occasion on which any divergence of opinion between the medical member and the patient's RMO should be brought out[1]:

> *Well, I think you do need to have the discussion so that you can identify whether the doctor is going to disagree very strongly with what the RMO is saying.* (Pres 08)

There was universal agreement that the medical member's examination and oral report was both important and valuable. However, there were varying views on how best this information should be shared to avoid prejudicing the other tribunal members and the patient's case:

> *But the way I deal with that is I will ask the lay member whether they would prefer to hear from the doctor before the hearing or after it and most of them say they haven't got a strong view – it depends on circumstances quite a lot. There may be cases where it's helpful to hear quite a lot from a psychiatrist beforehand. It also depends how recently they've seen the patient.* (Pres 07)

> *Well it depends on the attitude of the president. You see some people take the view that the half-hour before the meeting is really to decide what form the tribunal should take, whether the patient should be questioned first or whether the doctor should be questioned first. Some people take the view that they don't want to hear from the medical member of the tribunal, and that's fine, I mean I'm quite happy with that. Others take the view they do want to hear a little bit about the preliminary examination, in which case they can hear but one has to be careful not to tell them what one thinks the answer is.* (MM 10)

In practice, in the majority of tribunals we observed, medical members provided a report of their examination. In only a few instances was this report minimal or non-existent:

> *I have met doctors who – say virtually nothing, just say you know, well 'My findings of my examination will come out in the tribunal' and to some extent they do.* (LM 05)

This is one of the rare examples in which the medical member provided no report on their examination at all.

> *Pres* ➜ *Have you anything to add?* (to the tabled reports).
> *MM* ➜ *No change.* (RB06)

Most reports provided by the medical members included a fairly detailed picture of the patient's history, both prior to admission and since detained on the ward, symptoms during examination, and treatment. In addition, some medical members provided a report on the patient's treatment plan. From the *Guide* (1996b), it was clear that the art of being a medical member was to confine these reports to a straightforward account of these factors without commenting on or giving the other tribunal members an indication of whether the patient should be discharged:

> *... because the medical member has to do a preliminary examination, and because the chairman always begins by asking you what your impressions are, inevitably you find yourself giving an account of what your initial impressions are. But, I try to do it hopefully by indicating what I think might be the area that's going to be, need to be examined carefully, rather than actually giving the impression of having formed an opinion, as it were, of whether the section is in fact still justified.* (MM 22)

> *In practice, in almost all the tribunals I've attended, the medical member has gone over his or her examination of the patient in some detail beforehand, has kind of given a thumbnail sketch of how the patient appeared and what their concerns were and what the outcome of the interview was in terms of whether the doctor was confident of the diagnosis, and generally how the patient presented.* (LM 05)

Medical members frequently found that the very nature of this report, what was left in and what was left out, implicitly reflected their view of the patient's condition in relation to discharge. So conscious of this were some members that, in the interviews, they described strategies to promote 'a more objective' account of their examination:

> *And so what I now do before every tribunal I now get hold of a sheet of paper and just write down what I would recommend if I was doing an independent report ... So it's something a bit more objective ... What it is, why it's required, who determines it, that sort of thing. And then I can give that to the tribunal. I mean just glance at it.* (MM 21)

Given the role of the medical member as both a fact-finder and decision-maker, this conflict was not surprising. However, we observed many tribunals in which the lack of rules governing the medical member's report led to the production of highly influential contributions. On occasions this practice was openly acknowledged:

> *Pres* ➜ *Do we need to know anything more about these people?*
> *MM* ➜ *I'm not impressed, I know I shouldn't say anything in advance about my opinion on discharge. I don't see why I shouldn't say. If you are going to be swayed by my opinion I won't.* (RB01)

Inevitably, and not surprisingly, most medical members recognised that through their examination of the patient they had formed an opinion one way or another about the patient and their suitability for discharge. Whether they were asked to suspend this opinion or not depended on the president:

> *One is not supposed to give one's final opinion before the tribunal is actually in process ... If you're asked 'doctor is the patient round the bend?, are you recommending a discharge?' you're not supposed to say... anything about that but I often do. I say 'the patient is bonkers and um, really I would never at present, I wouldn't release him at present'. Er, that is, one shouldn't do that. I don't always do it. In fact I don't often do it but I do do it sometimes.* (MM 06)

The reports provided by medical members were influential in one of three ways:

- an indirect opinion as to the patient's suitability for discharge;
- a direct opinion as to the patient's suitability for discharge;
- a framework within which to interpret the patient's evidence.

Indirect opinions

In over half of all tribunals, the medical member gave an indication of whether or not, in their opinion, the patient should be discharged. Most commonly this was an indirect statement:

> *MM* ➔ (of a patient on a section 2) *Assessment is not yet complete.* (RC02)
> *MM* ➔ *We are unlikely to discharge him anyway.* (RD01)
> *MM* ➔ *He would be impossible to assess outside the hospital because he wouldn't cooperate with treatment.* (RA04)

There were also instances in which the medical members reported on their own emotional response to the patient. Given the way in which tribunals respond to the nature of the risks associated with discharge, this was of particular significance when it concerned fear or a threat of violence:

> *MM* ➔ *I was very threatened by this man.* (RA12)
> *MM* ➔ *He looks like a thug under the influence of drugs. He is a very frightening fellow.* (RA14)
> *MM* ➔ *He is a scary young man.* (RD11)

The rare instances in which the medical member challenged the RMO's view of the patient's condition were often accompanied by an indication that the patient should be considered for discharge:

> *MM* ➔ *I couldn't find evidence of mental illness.* (RB13)
> *MM* ➔ *The patient may not actually be mentally ill.* (RC05)
> *MM* ➔ *There is a case for him to be discharged. It's borderline.* (RA05)
> *MM* ➔ *This patient is ideal for supervised discharge.* (RC07; RA13)

Direct opinions

Much less common and more worrying were the comments that related directly to whether or not the patient should be discharged:

> *MM* ➜ *There is no way should he come off section in my opinion.* (RC12)
> *MM* ➜ *There is no doubt that he needs to be in hospital.* (RA12)
> *MM* ➜ *The patient is completely bonkers.* (RB02)
> *MM* ➜ *He should not be discharged. He really is not well.* (RD12)

In this last tribunal (RD12), the president told the medical member that it was prejudicial to reveal her opinion in a such an open and straightforward way. The medical member appeared embarrassed and admitted that she had only been a member for a year, was not aware of the protocol and had not had any training.

An interpretative framework

There were many occasions on which the medical member, in providing an oral report on the patient, also provided an interpretative framework within which the patient's evidence would be heard. Given that the patient's perspective is absent until the hearing, it could be argued that this provides a balance to the proceedings. This was not the case in the tribunals we observed. The interpretative framework served to discount what the patient would subsequently say in the hearing. It was quite common for medical members to brief the other members before the hearing that the patient had 'learned their lines' or 'would give the right answers'. This could be, for example, deliberately not talking about delusions, demonstrating a 'pretended' understanding of their illness, or agreeing to take their medication. The emphasis was on alerting the other members to the patient's ability to create an impression favourable to discharge.

> *MM* ➜ *He's learned the drill. He sees through the standard questions.* (RA08)
> *MM* ➜ *My impression is that superficially he can say the right things.* (RD11)
> *MM* ➜ *She will deny her symptoms. She is quite clever.* (RD14)
> *MM* ➜ *His interpretation of events will be different from those of the RMO and his mother. The patient will blame the alcohol.* (RD15)
> *MM* ➜ *He will argue convincingly that he needs help with his drug abuse.* (RA05)

Only very rarely were the medical member's comments questioned or alternative interpretations put forward:

> *Pres* ➜ (to the medical member) *I'm not saying he isn't deluded, but there may be a grain of truth in what he was saying, don't you think?* (RA04)
> *MM* ➜ *His place is a tip. A sign of his mental disorganisation.*
> *Pres* ➜ *or just an untidy person?* (RD02)

It is difficult to assess the precise impact of these statements on the final decision. Their importance perhaps rests on:

(i) the fact that they emanate from the most influential member of the tribunal, and as such are accorded credence;
(ii) their contribution to a construction of the patient biased by the absence of the patient's perspective; and
(iii) the phenomenon that early opinions are thought to be highly influential in ultimate decisions (Bjork, 1972; Ross *et al.* 1975; see Chapter 10, discussion of findings).

In three cases, comments by the president confirmed that at least one member of the tribunal had decided on the tribunal outcome before the hearing had taken place.

> *Pres* ➜ *Five minutes and we'll proceed without him. It won't make any difference anyway.* (RC06)
> *Pres* ➜ *It sounds from the report that the RMO is going to say he needs longer. We can go with that if that's what he wants.* (RC10)
> *Pres* ➜ *It looks unlikely that he will get out today.* (RB06)

These observations were supported by the interview data.

> *I don't quite know how to put this but I think I feel that somehow very often the decision is already made before the hearing ... I shouldn't say that but I think it's true. But then it can be changed of course ...* (MM 21)

> *He gives you an opinion of his meeting with the patient and I suppose it does colour your view a little. I must say it does – actually it does for me – it's a matter of just trying to put it out of your mind and looking at it afresh.* (LM 01)

Independent reports

Under section 76 of the MHA 1983, patients may commission their own reports on their own mental health. Reports may be commissioned from any registered medical practitioner authorised by or on behalf of the patient. In this study, 3 of the 61 patients had commissioned independent reports. In one case the independent report was presented at the beginning of the tribunal hearing. In the other two cases the reports were circulated at the pre-hearing meeting. In these two instances, the medical members of the tribunals used their privileged position as medical expert to downgrade and cast doubt on the quality and value of the independent reports before the tribunal. This was done in a globally dismissive way without recourse to the content of the reports. The reports were dismissed as not worth reading:

MM ➜ *I don't know why they bought an independent report. It's a waste of money.* (RD07)

In another case the report's status was challenged on the basis that the author was not a real doctor but was a clinical psychologist:

MM ➜ *That's not a psychiatric report.*
Clerk ➜ *No, he's a clinical psychologist.*
MM ➜ *Well I don't know if that's any value to the tribunal, I don't even know whether I will look at it.*
(begins to read it)
MM ➜ *A lot of this is totally irrelevant.*
(pres laughs)
Pres ➜ *What does the conclusion say?*
(clerk replies to doctor)
Clerk ➜ *You always say that, doctor.*
MM ➜ *They try to be doctors.*
Clerk ➜ *You just don't like their opinions.*
MM ➜ *Well, self-report questionnaires are of limited use* (referring to a section of the report which is based on a standardised assessment tool).
MM ➜ *He's not coming is he? I wish he was, I'd like to ask him some questions.* (RA07)

(ii) Legal issues

A number of discussions within the pre-hearing meeting arose from uncertainty over the correct legal position. These were issues which usually involved a number of questions over routine procedure which were fairly easily solved. They included:

- questions about who could be excluded from a tribunal (RA08; RC06);
- whether a tribunal could take place without a prior examination of the patient by the medical member (RA07 (see below); RA14);
- whether a tribunal could take place without a patient being present (RB09; RA11);
- whether a tribunal could take place without a patient being legally represented (RB09; RC03; RB04);
- whether the medical member had to undertake another assessment of the patient if the tribunal were adjourned because the patient was not able to attend (RA11);
- whether a tribunal could take place without the RMO report (RA01);
- whether a tribunal should go ahead if the legal representative had only been appointed the day before (RB14);
- whether a tribunal could go ahead if the section papers were incorrectly completed (RD09: RD12);
- questions about the disclosure of evidence (see RD14 below).

Different strategies were adopted to resolve these questions. The two first and most common strategies were:

- consultation of Jones's *Mental Health Act Manual*; and
- discussion between members and the clerk.

In one tribunal, a medical member had not managed to examine the patient:

> *MM* ➜ *Shall I tell you about the patient?*
> *Pres* ➜ *Yes please.*
> *MM* ➜ *Well I can't, she declined to see me.* (RA07)
> *(*He suggests that the tribunal could proceed on the basis of an examination of the medical notes. However, the clerk intervenes and persuades the medical member to 'have another go'. The medical member shows great reluctance but the clerk persists, eventually offering to go and talk to the patient herself. The clerk elicits the patient's consent who insists that her refusal had initially been based on a misunderstanding. The medical member goes off to carry out the examination.*)*
>
> *MM* ➜ *It will take at least an hour. I could do a quick ten minute but it won't be any use. All the information is in the reports.*
> *(*When the medical member has left the room, the president turns to the lay member and says*)*
> *Pres* ➜ *Without it we would be wide open to judicial review.* (RA07)

In another tribunal the disclosure of evidence became an issue as the significance of the evidence became apparent:

> *MM* ➜ *Do you want to see the medical notes as evidence? She will deny her symptoms.*
> *Pres* ➜ *I don't see why not.*
> *(*The medical notes are brought in and the president and lay member flick through the pages.*)*
>
> *MM* ➜ *They clarify her previous admissions during the previous 12 months.*
> *LM* ➜ *She was only out about one month.*
> *MM* ➜ *The RMO is a woman. She is off with flu, so it's the SHO, but she only came back from holiday yesterday, so she's not going to be very helpful. She's not very experienced.*
> *Pres* ➜ *I am beginning to be not very happy about this because we are seeing stuff I'm sure they've not had access to. Are they allowed to see the notes? Should we have been able to see them? Should we have got permission from the patient?*
> *LM* ➜ *There's not much extra in them.*
> *MM* ➜ *Yes there is, there's lots of clinical stuff. We could get round it by questioning the doctor and showing her the notes during the hearing to 'refresh' her memory.*

Pres ➜ (speaks to the clerk) *Can you take these and check whether the doctor has definitely seen them. I'm not happy.* (pauses) *They are from about a year ago.*
(The clerk goes off to speak to the doctor. When she returns she reports that the barrister who observed her talking to the doctor about the notes now wants to see the notes. A discussion ensues in which the members establish that the notes belong to the patient and the hospital. They are unsure whether an application has to be made to a hospital manager or whether the SHO can be asked 'to vet them', 'filleting them should anything need to be removed'. Any dispute is avoided when the SHO gives permission for the notes to be viewed by the patient and the barrister.) (RD14)

The Rules are specific on the patient's right to respond to undisclosed information (rule 12) that is seen by the tribunal and any material[2] should be presented to the patient prior to the hearing.

The discussion arising from consideration of the legal issues in the pre-hearing meeting demonstrated some surprising gaps in knowledge on the part of tribunal members. However, the information deficit was fairly quickly and easily resolved.

(iii) Social issues

The questions most frequently raised, often in the form of rhetorical questions, related to the social circumstances of the patient. The majority of those questions related to how the patient managed in the community:

LM ➜ *How has he been managing to look after himself?* (RB05)
LM ➜ *How does she answer the phone, given her mental state?* (RD05)

These questions were rhetorical because it was known in advance that the answers could not be gleaned from the reports nor from the medical member's assessment of the patient in hospital. Whether these issues were pursued in the hearing will be discussed later.

Summary

In the case of section 2 hearings the pre-hearing meeting provided time in which the tabled written reports could be read for the first time. In the case of section 3 hearings, according to the interview data, the RMO and social circumstances reports had been read before the pre-hearing meeting.

The pre-hearing meeting offered tribunal members the opportunity to clarify any uncertainties arising from a reading of the written reports and allowed members to identify the main issues to be pursued in the hearing. However, in the majority of tribunals, there was no discussion of the central issues arising from the written reports provided by the RMO and social worker, even though it was recognised in the interviews as one of the main purposes of the meeting. Without agreement in advance about the issues, evidence was often revealed and considered in a haphazard way and inconsistencies in reports remained unsolved.

The pre-hearing meeting was also the opportunity in which the majority of medical members were asked to provide an oral report on their examination of the patient. In the interviews, the tribunal members demonstrated some uncertainty over the nature and amount of information that a medical member could reveal. In a very small number of cases the report given by the medical member was extremely brief. The majority of reports provided by the medical member provided a fairly detailed account of the patient's history, symptoms during examination and treatment. In a minority of tribunals the medical member provided a report on the patient which either explicitly or otherwise indicated whether or not the patient should be discharged.

Notes

1 The *Guide* states that the medical member 'must appreciate that he performs a dual role at the tribunal as a fact-finder and decision-maker and it is therefore essential that his opinion of the patient's mental condition, if it differs significantly from that of the RMO, should be made known to everyone present in the course of his questioning. Thus a situation will be avoided where the members of the tribunal are acting on the basis of evidence known only to themselves, which would of course, be a breach of a fundamental principle of natural justice and likely to invalidate the decision (*Guide for Members*, 1996b, p. 49).

2 In brief, the 1990 Access to Health Records Act provides (with some exceptions) general rights of access to health records – information relating to the physical or mental health of an individual, made by or on behalf of a health professional in connection with the care of that individual. Access may, however, be refused where the information's disclosure would be likely to cause serious harm to the physical or mental health of the patient. Statutory applications to a local authority or health service authority take around 40 days to process and can therefore be of little use in a section 2 tribunals. It is not uncommon for patient/legal representatives to negotiate access directly with an RMO.

6

The Hearing

This chapter examines the process by which evidence was elicited during the tribunal hearing. It explores in some detail the nature of the RMO and patient evidence, and highlights the information considered crucial for decision-making. The way in which the evidence, once elicited, was interpreted is the subject of the following chapters.

Unless patients request otherwise, hearings are held in private. The *Guide for Members* (1996b) states that the tribunal has general discretion to conduct the proceedings in a manner that is considered most suitable in the light of each case.

All hearings were conducted in an informal and sensitive manner. All the members were introduced by name to the patient and the independence of the tribunal from the hospital was always stressed. The president invariably described how they were going to proceed and checked with the patient whether they wanted to be addressed and referred to by their first name or by their title and surname. During the course of the hearing, patients' requests for time out, a cigarette, or a glass of water were dealt with sympathetically and without hesitation. In the majority of tribunals, hearings were clerked from the beginning to the end and this seemed to facilitate greatly the tribunal's ability to accommodate simple patient requests without interrupting the flow of the proceedings.

Of the 61 observed tribunals, three were held without the patient being present. In all cases the patient had been examined by the medical member and all three cases concerned patients whose cases were being automatically reviewed. Automatic reviews take place under section 68 of the Mental Health Act (1983). In those instances in which the patient does not exercise the right to apply to a tribunal the hospital managers have a duty to refer the patient to a tribunal to ensure that detention is kept under regular independent review.

In the three cases where the patient did not appear at the tribunal there was discussion both in the pre-hearing meeting and at the beginning of the hearing about whether this was permissible within the legislation. Rule 22 (4) (MHRT Rules 1983, SI 1983 No. 942) provides that a tribunal 'shall in particular hear and take evidence from the applicant, the patient'. In all these cases the medical member supported the view that while the patient's detention should be reviewed in the interests of the patients' mental health they should not be obliged to attend the hearing.

Table 6.1 *Average length of time spent in the hearing stage of the tribunal (recorded in minutes)*

Stages of hearing	Region 1	Region 2	Region 3	Region 4	Average across all regions
Main hearing (average timing in minutes)	83	56	100	62	75

A clear picture did not emerge in the interviews with tribunal members as to whether a tribunal could be heard in the patient's absence. Most respondents were uncertain but thought it could. A few members thought that the only mechanism for this to be achieved lawfully was through excluding the patient under one of the rules (rule 21(4))[1].

In seven tribunals the patient left the hearing once it had started. In only one of these cases was the patient's premature departure planned and calm. In all other instances the patient left the hearing in a state of emotional distress, angry or tearful. Three patients were not represented by a solicitor or barrister. One of the patients without legal representation did not attend the tribunal (see above). In this case the tribunal was conducted without any patient representation or evidence except that produced through the medical member's prior examination of the patient.

Three patients had commissioned independent psychiatric reports, one of which was presented at the start of the hearing, while the other two had been tabled at the pre-hearing meeting.

Hearings across all the regions took an average of 75 minutes (see Table 6.1). In total, 24 tribunals lasted less than an hour, 30 tribunals took longer than one hour but less than two hours and 7 tribunals took more than two hours. In some regions, members were regularly booked for a number of tribunals to follow one after another. We observed occasions on which as many as three tribunals were to be carried out by the same team on the same day, often not in the same location. This created an additional set of pressures on members. In controlling the proceedings, a key objective was to ensure that the hearing was 'short'. One president noted in the interviews that this was also one of the main messages they had picked up during their induction:

> *The attitude was very much that if you were going to chair a hearing and it lasted longer than an hour you'd lost control of it.* (Pres 07)

The process by which information was elicited

Previous research has highlighted the adversarial nature of tribunals (Hepworth, 1983a). In both the interviews and the observations, the preferred approach to evidence gathering was inquisitorial:

> *We have a system, we refer to it being adversarial which, theoretically anyway, is designed to establish the truth of the witnesses' evidence... I suspect in a lot of the cases involving people's health that's not the main consideration or a particularly helpful test. So procedure designed to elicit the truth is not necessarily the right one.* (Pres 07)

> *Well we don't have any adversarial hearings at all. I understand that in X [another Region] they are more adversarial, although I have no first hand experience of it. I would have thought that wouldn't serve any purpose. I mean you're there for the interests of the health and safety of the patient and the safety of the public and I wouldn't have thought that you would get any closer to the truth of the matter by having an adversarial approach.* (Pres 13)

Although there were occasions during a small number of hearings in which RMOs and patients appeared to feel defensive or threatened, the overall approach was to ask questions as sensitively, sympathetically and politely as possible. All members were conscious of the need to preserve the RMO/patient relationship and the family/friend/patient relationship; and this created boundaries that members did not cross. Consequently there were circumstances in which the information being sought was not delivered. Some presidents recognised the danger of taking this approach too far: 'turning the tribunal into a case conference' was not seen to be the point of the process (Pres 13).

Ordering of witnesses

All members in the interviews emphasised the importance of the patient's evidence, and the order in which evidence was heard. However, as previously discussed, discussion in the pre-hearing meeting about the order in which a patient's evidence would be heard was limited and only explicitly took place in about one third of the observed tribunals.

There was a general view, expressed through the interviews, that each region had different preferred methods of ordering evidence. The patient was either heard first or last, or occasionally, if the circumstances demanded, both first and last. Notwithstanding the need for flexible arrangements, tribunals in two regions usually heard evidence from the patient first, whereas in the other two regions, the patient's evidence was taken last. In practice, the prevailing norm for the region was consistently observed.

There were equally valid and clearly articulated rationale for whichever course of action was adopted.

Hearing the patient first

In half of all observed tribunals, the patient's evidence was taken first. Two main categories of reasons for this were identified in the interviews. They related:

- to perceptions of entitlement and fair process; and
- to the mental state of the patient.

> *I have very strong feelings about it. I think the patient should always go in first … it's their liberty and I think one should hear what they have to say.* (Pres 13)

> *I mean the purest argument is it's the patient's application so he should go first, but the patient's representatives always want to do things differently.* (MM10)

One president thought that hearing the patient first was important for 'crystallising' the issues:

> *If I've got up-to-date reports, I actually prefer to hear the patient first, because at the end of the day, their evidence is probably going to be the most important, certainly on issues of insight and ongoing medication and all those things. So, I think it's helpful to hear from them first and then you can actually say to the doctor: 'He's saying he'll stay informally, why don't you believe it?' and you can actually crystallise the issues by hearing the patient first.* (Pres 08)

It was also recognised that, for some patients, listening to professionals making a case for their continued detention could prove to be too much of an ordeal:

> *I think sometimes it's rather alarming for patients to be talked about for two hours and they don't say a word and then they're asked something. They're talked about as if they're not there and therefore it may be a good idea to get them to have a word first.* (MM06)

> *… for a very disturbed patient, for instance, it's probably better not to take medical evidence first, because they get very upset.* (MM04)

Equally persuasive arguments were advanced by members who believed that hearing the patient last was important.

Hearing the patient last

On the other hand, hearing the patient last was also considered to be fairer. Enabling patients to hear what was being said about them allowed the patient's legal representative to counter the arguments:

> *I think it's best for the doctor to go first because it's better to hear the evidence for the prosecution which can then be answered by the defence.* (MM 10)

> *I think it's helpful for them as it were, to hear the case against them before they speak.* (LM05)

> *I believe that the patient should come last because they should have an opportunity to know what everyone has said about them. So that they can have the last bite of the cherry.* (Pres 01)

One member believed that the case against the patient should be made first, since the patient was being detained against his will.

> *I therefore tended to view it that the case against him should be heard first. And that it were much fairer to the patient to look at it in the light that here you have somebody who's being held against his will – detained, and who should therefore have the case against him made.* (Pres 02)

One of the dangers of hearing the evidence from the patient last was highlighted as one of the possible advantages. One medical member suggested that by the time the patient gets to speak at the end of the tribunal the outcome may well be clear.

> *He [a regional chairman] likes to have the patient at the very end. And it occurred to me that there was a lot of value in that actually because by that time it's all tied up.* (MM21)

A flexible approach

Most members interviewed expressed a preference for hearing the patient either first or last. However, all agreed that in certain circumstances they would change their preference:

> *Unless a doctor says: 'Look, I went to examine the patient – this patient is not going to sit through a hearing' – in which case we'd change the order and have the patient on first, and then maybe, you know, if anything emerges, have them on again at the end.* (Pres 01)

> *One or two have said it's a very good thing to adapt the procedure. So I normally try and discuss it before the tribunal begins to see whether anybody's got any views about who should go first.* (Pres 07)

It was clear, however, that a flexible approach could not be instituted without some discussion during the pre-hearing meeting. In most tribunals in which the order of evidence was mentioned, there was no clear statement of procedure. There was usually an opportunity for other members to argue for a different order. Exchanges usually involved a statement from the president of an intended course of action, quickly followed by a question:

> *Pres* ➜ *My view is we always have the patient first, any objections?* (RA06)

In theory this created an opportunity for both lay members and medical members to discuss the ordering of witnesses. However, in practice the question was usually directed at the medical member. The act of physically turning to talk to the medical member effectively blocked out the lay member. In our observations there was not a single occasion on which the lay member responded to this question. Thus, in all the interviews, and in the observed tribunals in which it was raised as an issue, medical members were seen as central to any deviation from the prevailing norm:

> *I usually ask the doctor whether they feel the medical evidence should come first or whether they think the patient will find that difficult and the patient should give their evidence first.* (Pres 08)

> *Pres* ➔ *I usually start with the doctor and give the patient the last word. (*turns to medical member*) Is he going to be stroppy?* (RA15)

> *Pres* ➔ *I am going to hear from the RMO first and then the social worker and then the family and then the patient, unless you (*turning to MM*) persuade me otherwise.* (RD01)

There were, however, instances in which the medical member did not wait to be asked and asserted a 'best course of action':

> *MM* ➔ *If she comes, she should be heard first.* (RB04)

Of course, the president did not have to follow the medical member's advice although it was usually taken. In one tribunal, the medical member suggested that the patient's evidence be taken first.

> *MM* ➔ *I suggest you start with the patient because if you start with the RMO, he will be pitching in all the time.* (RB03)

The president, however, ignored this request and the tribunal began with the evidence from the RMO. Five minutes into the tribunal the patient stormed out of the hearing. The medical member turned to the president as the legal representative ran out of the room after the patient and said, 'I did tell you to take his evidence first' (RB03).

In the above instance, it was not clear why the president decided not to follow the medical member's recommended course of action. One president in the interviews provided a possible reason:

> *I think particularly from a lawyer's point of view, in court you know that if you're the person making the application you start and the person against you making the application goes on next. And this is all part of our training. To then suddenly be placed into a situation where it can vary enormously depending on what anybody wants or the RMO's got to get off or whatever, well – it's difficult.* (Pres 20)

Introductions at the beginning of the hearing

In all tribunals, the order in which the evidence was to be taken formed part of the president's introduction. In this way both the members and the witnesses were informed of the procedure at the same time. Clearly, the ordering of the procedure was effectively only open for discussion by the legal representatives and the patient's RMO:

> *The ordering of the evidence is usually an issue which comes up between the advocate and the president. It's not an issue that we, other members of the tribunal, take a big part in.* (MM21)

In only one instance did an RMO ask for a change in the order of evidence. He wanted to be released from the tribunal after his evidence and did not want to wait until the end to give his evidence. The president did not agree to this request and the RMO stayed until the end of the hearing.

Similarly, although the opportunity existed, it was rare for legal representatives to request a reconsideration of the order of evidence:

> *I say to the solicitor 'look I think the best thing is for the RMO first, then the social worker, … then any family or friends, and then your client'. Because by then you will have heard everything that's being said about him. You can have one grand slam and tidy it all up … Now if you don't want to do it that way, then of course I'm amenable to doing it a different way.* (Pres 19)

It was clear that the order of the evidence was considered an important part of conducting a fair tribunal. However, there was no consensus on the fairest way of conducting the tribunal. One consequence of hearing the patient first, not mentioned in the interviews but evident in the observed tribunals, was that the RMO was required to be present throughout most of the tribunal hearing. The significance of this will be discussed in the next section under the RMO evidence.

Establishing evidence during the hearing

Although in all of the observed tribunals there were opportunities for all those attending to contribute to the evidence, some contributions were considered more important and were allocated more time. For instance, the interaction between the medical member and the RMO was seen as central to the tribunal's decision, while evidence from other witnesses, the social worker, nurse, family or friends, was in our observations more rushed and less thorough. The importance attributed to the patient's evidence varied.

RMO evidence

The RMO's evidence is effectively the main case for continuing detention. As one president commented in the interviews, 'We couldn't survive without RMOs. We have to have the RMO. We couldn't justify detention otherwise' (Pres 02).

In most cases the patient's RMO attended the tribunal but occasionally a more junior member of staff (registrar or senior house officer) deputised for the RMO.

Medical members were usually responsible for eliciting the evidence from the RMO and in doing so, they tended to adopt two different approaches. The first was to treat the hearing as a review of the patient's case, an opportunity for two doctors to compare notes. The second was a more confrontational approach, to test the RMO's evidence and the basis of their opinion. The second approach was less common but was obviously very important where the medical member disagreed with the RMO's opinion (in practice this was very rare). Several medical members were, however, prepared to be very critical of RMOs, particularly where it was felt that they had not prepared for the hearing, or were hostile to the idea of their opinion being challenged by the tribunal. As one medical member said:

> *I expect them to produce answers to the questions and if they can't I expect them to explain why they can't.* (MM03)

The RMO is given a privileged position at the tribunal, often being allowed to leave after giving evidence:

> *There is a sort of unspoken kind of law, rule, that the doctor should be allowed to go after they've given evidence but this is not usually offered to other people ... I really do object to it very strongly because the RMO is given notice of the tribunal. I know often one is busy, but as I said to you earlier it's this thing of not giving it enough weight. To my mind it's more important than other things that they have to do and they should make arrangements accordingly with other members of their team so I prefer them to stay. I think it is insulting really to their patient.* (MM03)

In allowing the early departure of the RMO, the tribunal recognises the workforce difficulties operating within mental health care services and the competing demands on RMO time. In the interviews, there was, however, a commonly expressed view by tribunal members that RMOs viewed the tribunal as an imposition on their time and on their professional judgement and integrity. As such they were to be tolerated but not viewed positively. The status of the RMO was emphasised by one president who noted that you had to be very brave to stop an RMO from leaving. The early departure of the RMO from the hearing meant that the RMO was not subsequently available to provide additional information or clarification of matters at a later stage if needed. It also meant that they were absent for the patient's evidence. RMOs were usually present at the beginning of the tribunal, and so on those occasions on which the patient's evidence was taken first they were present for the patient's evidence.

Questioning the witnesses

The evidence gathered from the RMO was elicited in the context of the statutory criteria – all RMOs were asked whether the patient's condition was of 'a nature or degree' which made them liable for detention in hospital. RMOs were either asked to respond to each element of the section 72 statutory criteria for discharge or were asked a more general question such as:

> *MM ➜ Could you indicate those features for formal purposes which lead you to conclude that he needs to be in hospital?* (RD10)

The discussion of the patient's condition thereafter developed according to the way in which these early questions were answered. The central issues which members explored routinely with RMOs were the presence or absence of:

- symptoms;
- insight;
- compliance and cooperation;
- risk and danger of the patient to other people.

In addition, members also tried to establish the nature of any improvement in the patient's condition that might have taken place. In particular, they were interested in how stable the improvement was.

The presence or absence of symptoms

In over half the cases, the evidence from RMOs concerning symptoms was backed up by the patient's behaviour during the tribunal. Loss of control in the hearing, with patients shouting, becoming emotional or leaving the room, were all taken as evidence of continued mental illness. Whether these symptoms were sufficient to warrant detention in hospital was dependent on additional evidence elicited under the other headings identified above.

Where the patient did not demonstrate any symptoms, members faced very real difficulties in establishing a clear picture from the RMO of the patient's condition. In many cases this was because the nature of the condition was complex. But there were also other confounding features of the RMO's evidence.

In a few tribunals, members tried to explore the boundaries between a mental illness and the patient's personality:

> *LM ➜ This severe maladjustment, does it play a part in diagnosis?*
> *RMO ➜ No, what underlines the behavioural problem is this – she is a lively, intelligent, rather mischievous young woman – although funny she is slightly delinquent. She overpowers patients in the unit. She can't stand people leaving. The maladjustment is therefore separate from the psychosis.*

(In the deliberation the members continued to wrestle with the implications of the RMO's evidence, unable to decide whether to place the emphasis on mental illness or stage of the lifecycle.)

Pres ➜ *She behaved impeccably. It's very distressing, you're so worried about whether it's a mental problem or a very severe teenage problem.* (RB15)

As Wood (1970) notes, confinement leads to all sorts of behaviours that require some interpretation to assess the extent to which they are important or trivial matters and the extent to which they are provoked. There were many examples in which a patient's behaviour was defined by an RMO as a 'symptom' of a mental disorder. In the case previously cited (RB15), the tribunal remained unconvinced about the linkage of the behaviour to a disorder. At the end of the deliberation, the president side-stepped the attribution of the behaviour to the disorder by simply stating that the behaviour and the disorder co-existed, i.e. that the patient suffered from a mental disorder and also behaved inappropriately.

In some cases, problems raised by complex mental health problems were compounded by the apparent inability of an RMO to answer questions as posed:

LR ➜ *Is his condition of a nature or degree that warrants detention?*
RMO ➜ *There is just one reason. In November when I asked him to come and see me and take his medication he didn't. He is not compliant. He was under section 37 and was on remand and he has never been compliant.*
(president intervenes)
Pres ➜ (to the RMO) *The legal representative wants to concentrate on the current situation, is it nature or degree?*
RMO ➜ *He has been aggressive, but is not compliant.*
LR ➜ *Is he treatable in the community?*
RMO ➜ *I would like to but he is not ready yet.*
LR ➜ *Is it of a nature or degree?*
RMO ➜ *Both.*
LR ➜ *Are you assessing or treating him?*
RMO ➜ *Both at the moment.* (RA08)

In another case the RMO was openly hostile to the members' questioning. When asked about aspects of the patient's care and treatment he replied that he was unable to help the tribunal as he had only recently taken on the patient's case and had not written the RMO report they had before them. His manner was aggressive 'to the point of rudeness' as the tribunal president commented in the deliberation. None of the lines of questioning produced any helpful answers and an analysis of the tribunal transcript showed the phrase 'I can't assist you with that' to have been repeated on ten separate occasions in response to questioning. The statement 'I don't know the patient well enough' was repeated five times (RC12). As soon as the questioning of the RMO was finished, the RMO abruptly got to his feet and left the room, without signalling or requesting permission that he be allowed to leave. The tribunal members were so offended by his behaviour that the researchers were asked not to record the subsequent conversation.

The above illustration was the only case in which the RMO's attitude was hostile throughout the whole of the tribunal. It was far more common for RMOs to respond to particular questions in a defensive way. Reports containing inaccuracies and challenges to medical evidence (discussed below) were the most common triggers of a defensive or aggressive response:

> *MM* ➜ *How did (*reads from report*) 'impulsive and severe threat to own safety' get into the report?*
> *RMO* ➜ *It got into the report because it is repeated so often, that it was dictated in an unthinking manner. You know how you say 'impulsive and severe threat to own safety' 'compliant under order but not otherwise'.*
> *MM* ➜ *Mmm, yes I do know how it is but I don't think I want to go into it.* (RD02)

In the above tribunal, the allegation that the patient was a threat to his own safety appeared in the RMO's report. The RMO admitted that this was not true and the patient's legal representative requested that the report be rewritten for the file without the inaccurate remark.

In another tribunal the inaccuracy of the RMO's statement created the impression that the RMO was deliberately trying to mislead the members:

> *MM* ➜ *What is meant by – he continually smokes cannabis?*
> *MM* ➜ *Did he continually smoke cannabis in here?*
> *RMO* ➜ *No.*
> *MM* ➜ *Did you do a drug test?*
> *RMO* ➜ *Yes.*
> *MM* ➜ *So what is meant by continually smokes, if he is not doing it in here?*
> *RMO* ➜ *He did smoke at home, he continued to smoke at home.*
> *MM* ➜ *So, not here. It is grammatically incorrect in the report.*
> *RMO* ➜ *No, not here.* (RB01)

There were also a few instances in which the patient's cases were so complex that additional evidence, had it been available, would have enabled the tribunal members to be more confident one way or another of the 'real situation':

> *I think the short answer is that we would actually accept it [*evidence*], essentially unquestioning. Unless there was some reason for questioning it, we would accept it. Unless something conflicted with it. If the patient says, 'No I didn't throw the glass', well then we would have to try and weigh up – 'Is this a point on which the whole case turns?' and if it is – I mean, if the whole risk element is tied up in this one 'throwing of a glass', well then we may say, either 'this is very important, this throwing of the glass, let's try and get to the bottom of it', or you may say, 'does really one throwing of a glass create such an element of risk that we can't discharge this patient?' It's unlikely that one thing of this nature would be sufficient. You'd be looking at a series of events. My experience is that when you come to a series what you find is not, 'I didn't throw the glass', but … 'I did throw it but it was an empty cup', or 'I did throw it, but it was at the wall'.* (Pres 02)

Some patients claimed to be engaged in complex legal battles. In three cases, much of the tribunal's time was spent trying to assess such claims. The initial line of questioning by the tribunal tended to suggest that the legal battles were a figment of the patient's mental condition. However, in one tribunal this view was overturned as some of the detail emerged and the legal battle was found to be real. Had the RMO considered that it was important to discount the legal case as a component of the patient's mental state, evidence would have been readily available from the solicitor acting on behalf of the patient. Because the RMO had not considered that establishing the veracity of the patient's claim was relevant to the patient's treatment, the tribunal, which considered that the patient's claim was relevant to his mental state, was diverted into establishing whether or not the legal battle was real.

> *LR* ➜ *Have you spoken to the patient's solicitor about his belief about his tenancy agreement and the legal dispute with his agency? Could there be a valid dispute?*
> *RMO* ➜ *No, I haven't made any investigation into it. It could be valid.*
> *LR* ➜ *Have you spoken to Mrs Black*[2] *(female friend of patient) about his social functioning?*
> *RMO* ➜ *Not at length. I know she feels he is well and has known him long enough.* (RD09)

The RMO evidence in section 2 hearings was particularly difficult to assess. The amount and quality of evidence presented by the RMO depended in part on how long into the detention the tribunal took place. However, in many instances members were unable to determine whether certain planned tests were really critical to the patient's diagnosis and treatment:

> *LM* ➜ *Your assessment – is it complete?*
> *RMO* ➜ *No. The diagnosis I am pretty confident of, but he needs some firming up on his treatment plan. It's virtually complete.*
> *Pres* ➜ *What further physical investigations are you planning?*
> *RMO* ➜ *Anaemia, protein and calcium deficiency tests.* (RD09)
> *MM* ➜ *Are you still involved in assessing her?*
> *RMO* ➜ *I would have to say that we are not able to assess her condition as fully as we would like.*
> *MM* ➜ *What further information do you require?*
> *RMO* ➜ *More nursing information. Her persecutory ideas are still present. We need a series of interviews to identify the consistency of the ideas expressed. With regard to her impairment of functioning we need to establish objective evidence that as a result of her mental disorder, her functioning is impaired.*
> *MM* ➜ *Are you planning further investigations?*
> *RMO* ➜ *Yes, a CT scan to exclude an organic component, and a diagnostic screen to check that we are not missing anything.*
> *MM* ➜ *There's no history of any organic illness?*
> *RMO* ➜ *No.* (RD08)

In the case of section 2 hearings, further tests pending raised the question in the minds of members as to whether the RMO was unnecessarily 'dragging the assessment out'. Members struggled in the deliberation to determine the additional benefits to be derived from further tests.

In one hearing, by chance, all members of the tribunal panel had specialist knowledge and expertise pertaining to the patient's case. This tribunal operated at a different level from any of the others observed. Punctilious and patient, they questioned the RMO closely, revealing inadequate and poorly thought through treatment plans. After an initial hearing, of just over two hours, the tribunal was adjourned pending assessment by the RMO of the patient's suitability for a mother–baby unit (see adjournment, pp. 74–5):

MM ➜ What about the mother–baby unit? Bonding is difficult when the child is taken away so quickly.
RMO ➜ Equally it is not easy, because at the moment we do not know whether it is something that she wants to do.
MM ➜ That's why they have specialist units.
RMO ➜ The vast majority of units have closed down. She has been in before when she was less distressed and she has not done well. The lack of success when she wasn't that unwell was caused by a post-partum exacerbation of symptomatology.
MM ➜ Has she been assessed for the mother–baby unit?
RMO ➜ I have discussed on the phone with the mother–baby unit. (RD13)

In this tribunal the RMO's perceived unwarranted reluctance to refer the patient to a specialist unit, combined with tribunal members' doubts about the ability of the current treatment setting to deal effectively with this mother and baby, led the tribunal to seek a way of improving the patient's circumstances while keeping her under section.

Insight

The concept of insight cropped up in the majority of hearings but was rarely explored. Its importance within psychiatry and hearings in general was recognised by all the members interviewed. There was less clarity about how the concept could be examined with any certainty during the hearing:

... It is used in I would have thought, 99 per cent of the cases – 'the patient has no insight' and that's seen to be a symptom of their illness that they don't understand that they're ill. Whereas there's another school of thought that says, you don't have to understand you're ill, you just have to understand that treatment makes you better. But I suppose there's a dilemma there – how can you understand it's going to make you better if you don't think you're ill in the first place? You need to have an insight and if you don't have an insight it's a symptom of an illness – sometimes the only symptom because all the other symptoms are in remission because of the drug therapy that people are taking. The only thing you have is whether the person understands that they've been ill. (Pres 01)

Members tended to accept the RMO's view that insight was deemed to be present, absent or partial. They had no independent strategies for assessing the extent to which those views were accurate:

MM ➜ How much insight?
RMO ➜ It's improved.
MM ➜ He told me that he wasn't ill.
RMO ➜ He has said that he's not here for no reason, so that's an improvement. (RB01)
MM ➜ Can you tell me about the patient's mental state today?
SHO[3] *➜ Yesterday, the patient showed little insight into the hospital's concerns. She had persecutory beliefs and admitted hearing voices sometimes.*
LR ➜ What do you mean by insight?
SHO ➜ It means she is unable to attribute symptoms to an illness. (RD14)
RMO ➜ Any insight would vaporise in a more unstructured environment. (RC03)

The links between insight and mental illness and between insight and compliance made the concept an important one.

Compliance and cooperation with treatment

Compliance and non-compliance with treatment regimes (both behavioural and pharmaceutical) were extremely significant issues in relation to discharge. They were the factors most frequently presented by RMOs as the reason for not discharging. Satisfactory evidence could rarely be produced about a patient's future compliance. Inevitably, there were assertions from RMOs and patients that could not be tested:

Pres ➜ The patient says he would comply, what is your opinion?
RMO ➜ It was an issue, but he is now certain that he would comply. He sees his time here as a sentence and compliance as a way of reducing that sentence, therefore I am not sure how much he would comply when he was out.
Pres ➜ He has said that he would come back and see you. Could he be treated outside of the hospital?
RMO ➜ At this stage, yes.
Pres ➜ What are the risks if section is lifted?
RMO ➜ Whether he can maintain compliance. I haven't had enough chance to try him at home since his improvement. (RC01)

It was assumed that non-compliance resulted from a lack of insight because a patient with insight would understand the importance of treatment and so cooperate with it.

Pres ➜ Can we infer lack of insight from lack of compliance?
RMO ➜ Yes. (RA04)

There were no circumstances in which an RMO considered non-compliance to be rational or acceptable. However, some patients did demonstrate quite rational reasons, based on insight and choice, for not taking their medication with weight gain and a dislike of side effects commonly cited as reasons for non-compliance. Moreover, patients frequently recognised and articulated in the tribunal the double bind they knew themselves to be in:

MM ➜ *Can we focus on your medication. You are on Modecate?*
Pt[4] ➜ *Yes, I'm not happy with it. My periods have stopped, so I am not getting rid of impurities. Lithium can be toxic. Also I am not big, but because of these psychiatric drugs I am bloated and shaky and I've developed a skin rash through the drugs. I know there is an adverse effect if I don't take them.*
MM ➜ *So why do you take them?*
Pt ➜ *I'd wean myself off them.*
MM ➜ *If you were a free agent – what would you do about medication?*
Pt ➜ *I can't see myself on my own. I've always been with my family.*
MM ➜ *Yes, but if you had a free choice?*
Pt ➜ *What do you mean?*
MM ➜ *Which would you stop first? Would you drop your droperidol and keep your lithium?*
Pt ➜ *I have never not taken them.* (RD06)

RMO ➜ *She is constantly asking for her medication to be reduced. She has become preoccupied with her weight gain over the last several years. She is reluctant to take medication when well.*
MM ➜ *What are the features of her mental illness?*
RMO ➜ *She is symptom free. She is in remission with rapid relapse if non-compliant.*
RMO ➜ *We have to be guided by what has happened in the past. The chances are she would stop taking her medication, and may well be influenced by her mother who is also concerned by her weight problem.* (RD01)

Neither of the young women in these tribunals was receiving any dietary advice, nor did the RMOs consider their concerns to be 'reasonable'. Even where the effects of the drugs were uncertain, compliance was still considered to be important:

MM ➜ *What are your plans for treatment?*
SHO ➜ *The RMO would like her to remain on section because he thinks the patient won't stay nor will take her medication. The RMO wants to consider introducing depot medication.*
MM ➜ *Do you feel satisfied that medicine is helping?*
SHO ➜ *It is difficult to say, but past patterns suggest that it does allow her back to full functioning.* (RD14)

A common theme to emerge in these tribunals was the importance of past behaviour as an indication of future behaviour. Past non-compliance invited a label of 'non-compliance' from which it was extremely difficult to depart:

> *RMO* ➜ *Looking to past behaviour and current attitudes there are questions over future compliance.* (RB12)
> *RMO* ➜ *If history is any guide for what may happen in the future, it is likely to happen again. She would fall apart in two weeks. If she were to continue with her medication that would provide extra protection. She would not collapse within two weeks.* (RB16)

Compliance could not be viewed separately from the consequences of relapse. In the tribunal mentioned above (RB16), the patient was severely depressed and had previously tried to smother both her young children before attempting suicide. Improvements gained through medication were felt to be critical to the safety and welfare of the patient and her family.

Risk

Risk of violence, principally to others but also to self, were major concerns of the tribunal. Across all tribunals, the evidence on risk was perhaps weakest. The appearance and presentation of the patient, and verbal aggression, contributed to perceptions of dangerousness. However, there was frequently little attempt to identify the nature of 'risk' with any accuracy. 'Good' legal representatives were particularly important in the process of establishing the nature, context and specifics of reported incidents and 'risks':

> *LR* ➜ *There is a mention of knives – what sort of knife?*
> *RMO* ➜ *It was on him when he was admitted – I don't know what sort of knife it was.*
> *LR* ➜ *A Hamleys' modelling knife?*
> *RMO* ➜ *I don't know.*
> *(*The knife was later confirmed by the social worker to be a modelling knife.*)*
> (RB01)

In questioning the witnesses at the hearing, the tribunal adopted a court-based approach, dealing with the evidence from each witness sequentially. All witnesses are gathered together in the same room and are questioned in turn. Tribunals do not adopt an issue-based approach to their evidence. That is, they do not sort out the issues in advance and question each witness on each issue, before moving on to the next issue.

While assessing whether a patient posed a risk was important, achieving a coherent picture of risk was difficult. Each new witness contributed a different bit of the picture, but it was rarely possible to achieve a comprehensive overview. Statements about alcohol, substance and drug abuse, for instance, were frequently accepted as fact without any real evidence to confirm or refute them:

MM ➔ *Do you have any concerns if he was discharged today?*
RMO ➔ *Yes, continuing inappropriate behaviour with women. He has shown an inability to learn and generalise from that. There are letters asking inappropriate questions of a sexual nature. And there was one particular incident in which he was staring at girls in a car, blocking their exit. He isn't violent. As a result I have discontinued his unescorted walks.*
MM ➔ *Why does he need to be detained under section?*
RMO ➔ *I don't think he will remain informal.*
MM ➔ *What do you think he will do?*
RMO ➔ *He will leave probably and go out and do something.*
MM ➔ *Where would he go? Would he leave the premises?*
RMO ➔ *He might just leave. When he is locked up he can't control himself.*
*(*The RMO creates the impression that the patient is not allowed any independent freedom of movement because of the risk he poses. Later on in the tribunal it emerges that patient does have unescorted leave, which the RMO accepts. He corrects his previous view stating that he had forgotten.*)*
LM ➔ *Patient says he does have unescorted leave now. Have you updated this?*
RMO ➔ *Yes, possibly, sorry.*
LR ➔ *He has not been harmful, physically recently?*
RMO ➔ *He is threatening to others.*
LR ➔ *Because of his size?*
RMO ➔ *Partly, but also it is the way he behaves.*
LR ➔ *So, there has been no actual risk to others?*
RMO ➔ *Well, the car park incident – I perceive there is a risk.*
LR ➔ *For the patient's own health and safety?*
RMO ➔ *I am concerned that he would aggravate a response in someone else.*
*(*By the time the legal representative questions the RMO, an impression has been created that the patient is both dangerous and not allowed out. Indeed, although the legal representative gets the RMO to retract his previous statement, in the deliberation the tribunal members remain of the view that he is dangerous.*)* (RB06)

In another tribunal (RA04) the tribunal applicant was a 35-year-old man who was detained under a section 2. He was diagnosed as having chronic paranoid psychosis, and his family said he had been ill for 16 years. He had been admitted to hospital once before (according to the RMO's report about 12 years previously). He was diverted to hospital from the magistrates court, following an alleged attack/harassment (unclear at hearing) on his (ex) girlfriend. The evidence presented on risk to others was largely reported from his (ex) girlfriend. She was not present but the RMO presented the girlfriend's allegations about an attack on her and on a priest. There was some concern that this was hearsay evidence; but the fact that the police had brought charges was considered relevant. The patient avoided answering questions about alleged violence, and this was also considered significant.

Improvement in condition

Some of the section 3 reports provided by RMOs were relatively old by the time of the hearing. The majority had been written between three and five weeks before the tribunal but some had been written as long ago as two months before the tribunal. It therefore made sense for medical members, when questioning the RMO, to begin with questions about the patient's recent mental health:

RMO ➔ I wrote the report two months ago. He has improved gradually. He has some leave, and although I am still concerned it is less so.
*MM ➔ So do you still stand by it? (*the report*)*
*RMO ➔ It is difficult to say of today but (*RMO appears to be thinking*)*
*(*MM interrupts the silence*)*
MM ➔ Any incidents at all recently?
RMO ➔ There was the incident with the knife in November.
MM ➔ Recovery seems pretty fast.
RMO ➔ Yes, since I changed his medication. (RD11)
*(*As the tribunal progresses it becomes more difficult to gauge exactly what progress has been made, since the current mental state appears to differ so dramatically from that described in the report and to be associated with a change in medication.*)*

RMOs were usually cautious about improvement and wanted some evidence of symptom stability before they felt confident about release. RMOs appeared particularly reluctant to take 'risks' with patients who were close to discharge and who had highly valued places in specialist accommodation:

MM ➔ Has he been better since he came here?
RMO ➔ Yes.
MM ➔ Is the degree severe enough for detention?
RMO ➔ It is debatable. He does show some symptoms of mental illness, some thought disorder, there were hints of it today. But all major symptoms are gone. The hostel is quite nervous about having him.
MM ➔ If he were to be liable to be recalled would that make them happier about having him?
RMO ➔ I haven't discussed it with them explicitly but I don't want to have him thrown out before he has been properly established. They don't normally insist on a one-month trial leave.
MM ➔ Is your real concern to keep him on section to ensure that he takes his medication in the community?
RMO ➔ Yes.
MM ➔ Is it the only reason?
RMO ➔ My other fear is that he will stay with his pals and although he wants to keep away from drugs it would be hard. It is more important to have somewhere suitable or not at all. (RB05)

LM ➜ *What do you expect to see?*
RMO ➜ *A consistent period where there is little indication of elevated depression.*
LM ➜ *What does consistent mean?*
RMO ➜ *I haven't had so much as a couple of weeks yet.* (RD10)

On the face of it, a tribunal's decision to discharge a patient is taken against the advice of the RMO. In the interviews, members raised the question of whether on occasions RMOs used the opportunity of the tribunal to share the responsibility of deciding whether or not to discharge the patient:

> *One sometimes feels that at a tribunal, that the RMO is actually dodging a decision and that he might have discharged earlier, but because the tribunal date is coming up he's not actually discharged and you sometimes feel it's being left to the tribunal to make the decision.* (Pres 14)

There were a few observed tribunals in which the RMO appeared to be genuinely uncertain about whether the patient was ready to be discharged or not:

RMO ➜ *Yes, I have completed my assessment. She is compliant with medication. I can't elicit any symptoms of psychosis. There was a point when she was very concerned about a member of staff and had another fear of being attacked by male patients. She has settled and is doing well.*
MM ➜ *What about the severity of her symptoms?*
RMO ➜ *She is doing well.*
MM ➜ *Does she warrant detention?*
RMO ➜ *I am sitting on the fence. I am mainly concerned about life outside the hospital. Maybe she would stop taking her medication as before.*
MM ➜ *Is that part of the nature of her illness? If she does go home and doesn't take her medication what would happen?*
RMO ➜ *She could relapse.*
*(*the president interrupts*)*
Pres ➜ *You say you are on the fence – which side would you say you were on?*
RMO ➜ *She warrants detention – just.*
Pres ➜ *And that's on grounds of risks of relapse if she doesn't comply?*
RMO ➜ *Yes.*
*(*legal representative interrupts*)*
LR ➜ *Is she displaying symptoms today?*
RMO ➜ *No.*
LR ➜ *Is she compliant with medication? Does she have insight?*
RMO ➜ *Yes, she is complaint and she has partial insight.* (RB07)
RMO ➜ *There is not a great deal in it either way. She has now settled. She has been preoccupied, which could be for all sorts of reasons. I found the recommendation part the hardest I have had to do. I would be reluctant to come to any conclusions.* (RC05)

These cases were some of the hardest for tribunal members to solve:

> *Pres* ➜ *It is always difficult when the doctor is lukewarm about keeping her in.* (RA09)

In the deliberations, some members tried to second-guess why the RMO had not discharged the patient. It was as though they thought there was some 'catch' to the RMO's indecision, something they did not know about, a risk that they would unwittingly take were they to decide to discharge the patient. They therefore spent some time trying to work out the RMO's reasoning.

Challenges to medical evidence

In some tribunals there were clear challenges to medical evidence. Not surprisingly, the most robust and concerted challenges to medical evidence came from legal representatives. There were also some articulate and confident patients who were not bound by the constraints of professional courtesy and who asked insightful and challenging questions.

Members did not always view these challenges as appropriate or productive. One medical member felt that the legal representative was asking questions beyond the tribunal's remit:

> *MM* ➜ *The RMO must have freedom of clinical judgement, we should not be having a discussion of the doctor's treatment of the patient.*
> *Pres* ➜ *It is for the president of the tribunal to say what should or should not be discussed.*
> *(*As the tribunal progresses the patient, an intelligent and articulate man, begins to ask questions.*)*
> *Pres* ➜ *These are questions which need to be raised with Dr X (his RMO) and his team.*
> *Pt* ➜ *(*turns to RMO*) What is the nature of my schizophrenia?*
> *RMO* ➜ *We should not be discussing this here.*
> *(*RMO then turns to the president of the tribunal*)*
> *RMO* ➜ *Is this your opinion?*
> *(*The president then turns to patient and says*)*
> *Pres* ➜ *Are you asking about your symptoms?*
> *Pt* ➜ *It's very important that you define what you mean by schizophrenia.*
> *MM* ➜ *We are not here to discuss individual mental illness. The technicalities of the type of mental illness you have should be discussed privately.*
> *LR* ➜ *If (*patient*) raises it here, it is because there are no other arenas in which he can get some sort of answer.*
> *Pres* ➜ *(*turning to RMO*) Can you tell him the sorts of symptoms he exhibits?*
> *(*The set of exchanges comes to an uncomfortable conclusion when the RMO says to the patient:*)*

RMO ➔ I think to discuss this further would be detrimental to our relationship, such as it is, in such an adversarial context. (RD02)

This response was interesting because the RMO's sense of being challenged had introduced an atmosphere of impending conflict, yet according to the rules of natural justice the tribunal is precisely the setting in which the patient can legitimately test the factual basis for the RMO's views.

Medical member challenges to the RMO's evidence were altogether less adversarial and less directly articulated:

MM ➔ I entirely agree with your clinical opinion, but from a legal perspective these are all 'mights'. There's no direct evidence is there?
RMO ➔ No, although you could say locking people in was threatening to them.
MM ➔ Wasn't he protecting them? (half laughing) *And his clothes are not falling off him!*
RMO ➔ I am concerned about the adequacy of his food. (RD09)

The patient's evidence

The tribunal's business is actually to assess the person as he is on the day of the tribunal and although they have to take into account what's happened in the past, it is the way the chap presents. That's really what you see. (MM 10)

All members were sensitive to the patient's mental state and alert to any signals during the hearing that might indicate that the patient's illness was of a nature or degree that made them liable to be detained. How the patient's evidence was brought out frequently depended on the skills of the legal representative as well as on the patient's mental state at the time of the hearing. However, there were instances when patients were dealt with as though they were trying to mislead members about their mental state. Members talked in the interviews and in the observed tribunals about the way patients unwittingly incriminated themselves by displaying symptoms of their illness. These ranged from a clear demonstration of thought disorder to withdrawal and expressions of desire to self-harm.

Where patients were deemed to have the capacity to 'perform well' – by 'hiding their symptoms' or by having 'learned their lines well' – tribunal members asked more probing questions (RA10). In a small number of the observed tribunals, attempts to establish 'the truth' or 'attitudes held by a patient' could be viewed as trying to 'catch them out'. Interestingly, we observed instances in which each type of tribunal member (medical, legal and lay) engaged in this 'catching out' technique (see also RD15 discussed in Chapter 8).

MM ➔ Do you think the police are against you?
Pt ➔ No – just diligent.
MM ➔ Why are they against you?
Pt ➔ I didn't say that. (RD14)

On the whole, tribunal members did not seem to approach their questioning of the RMO or the social worker in the same way.

The way in which the patient's evidence was discussed and interpreted in the deliberation will be the subject of Chapter 7.

Legal representatives

> *To provide rights for people to go to appeal before tribunals and so on is very much an empty exercise, unless at the same time one provides them with the kind of assistance which they undoubtedly need if they are to extract the full value from that process.* (Lord Winstanley, Hansard col. 787, 1982)

The knowledge, skills and abilities of the legal representatives observed in the tribunals varied considerably. Whether or not representation enabled patients to 'extract the full value' from the tribunal depended to a large extent on the legal representative's familiarity with the MHA 1983 and the nature, diagnosis and treatment of mental disorder. In the observed tribunals, not all legal representatives fulfilled these requirements and, after the hearing, members frequently discussed whether the solicitor/ barrister was a panel member[5].

Both in the interviews and the observed tribunals, presidents took a dim view of legal representation which undermined the patient and there was a general view that solicitors were there to represent the client and not 'to throw the case if they think it isn't worth running' (Pres 19). Members were not impressed by legal representatives who in private audience with the tribunal panel before the start of the tribunal were prepared to admit that their client had 'got a hopeless case' or that they themselves were not convinced by their client's case:

> *Pres ➔ The give-away is when he says my instructions are blah blah – then you know it's cobblers.* (RB11)

However, members were keen to identify whether the patient's application was for discharge or for some other purpose; for example, a request for reclassification or for transfer to another hospital. Hearing from the patient/legal representative enabled the tribunal to establish the boundaries within which their decision-making should take place:

> *By the time they've got to the tribunal hearing and discussed it with a lawyer they may not actually be asking for discharge any more, so it's helpful to have that clarified.* (Pres 14)

In this way members were relieved of the need to go beyond what was being requested in their decision-making. The disadvantages of not having a legal representative were exposed in one tribunal. The president indicated to the patient at the end of the hearing:

> *Pres* ➔ *We will probably keep you under section, although I cannot be certain because we have to discuss it.* (RC03)

When the patient had left the room the president said:

> *Pres* ➔ *Had there been a legal rep there he might not have been so accepting of his fate.* (RC03)

In one case the legal representative sought an adjournment. The patient had been sedated during the previous night and could not be roused for the start of the hearing at 11 a.m. The legal representative informed the president that her attempts to wake her client had resulted in an incoherent and partial conversation before the patient had turned over and gone back to sleep. The legal representative thought it unfair for the tribunal to proceed without the patient. The tribunal was adjourned for three days.

Adjournment

In a handful of cases the president adjourned the proceedings. The Rules state that a tribunal 'may at any time adjourn a hearing for the purpose of obtaining further information or for such other purposes as it may think appropriate' (rule 16(1)). Before adjourning any hearing, the tribunal may give such directions as it thinks fit for ensuring the prompt consideration of the application at an adjourned hearing (rule 16(2)).

As other authors have pointed out (Hepworth, 1983b), tribunals occasionally attempt to influence the care and treatment of the patient where they believe that a relevant course of action has not been pursued by the patient's RMO or the hospital. This occurred in two observed tribunals. The first tribunal has already been mentioned (RD13), and concerned the patient considered to be likely to benefit from transfer to a mother–baby unit. The RMO had very quickly given up a search for a place for her and was content to allow her to be separated from her new-born child indefinitely. At the end of a two-hour hearing, the patient's solicitor was invited to make a submission on her patient's behalf. She announced to a stunned tribunal that:

> *LR* ➔ *She wants to be discharged and remain as an informal patient. The tribunal should, however, be realistic so I find myself unable to make a submission on my client's behalf. I will leave it to the bench to decide.*
> *Pres* ➔ *Are you not putting forward any suggestions on your client's behalf?*
> *LR* ➔ *The patient wants to be discharged but she will stay in hospital. But you have to have regard for her mental condition and pay attention to the answers she gave. I therefore find myself not able to make a submission on her behalf.*
> (The president of the tribunal turns to the patient.)
> *Pres* ➔ *Do you want to add anything?*

Pt ➔ *No.*
*(*The patient and other witnesses all leave the room.*)*
*(*The members then spend a further hour trying to establish the best course of action. The possibility of adjournment emerges only after the statutory criteria have been discussed and is arrived at through their perceptions that the patient is receiving a poor quality of treatment and the untapped potential of treatment were she to be placed in a different setting. They record their decision to adjourn in the following way:*)*

We regard it as essential to the making of our decision that we have a report from a consultant psychiatrist in charge of a mother–baby unit as to the suitability of the patient to be admitted with her baby.
The tribunal's directions are as follows:
Directions
*An independent report must be obtained by the RMO from a consultant psychiatrist in charge of a mother–baby unit as to the patient's suitability for admission with baby. Such a report should be submitted to the tribunal office by xx/xx/xx (*date*).* (RD13)

A more straightforward case (RD01) concerned a young woman whose principal problem was non-compliance with her medication. She was intermittently non-compliant, she argued, mainly as a result of massive weight gain and feelings of being unattractive and unhealthy. The patient had expressed her concerns to health professionals for over a year but none of the agencies had tackled the problem. In frustration with a system which demanded her compliance, but which failed to recognise the cause of her non-compliance, the tribunal adjourned with the following direction:

*We are adjourning for the hospital to hold a s.117 meeting and arrange the transfer of the patient either to a community supervision order or into guardianship and particularly to refer her to the eating disorder unit at XX Hospital and an up-to-date medical and social work report to reach the office by xx/xx/xx (*date*).* (RD01)

Whether the direction was technically correct or not, the patient was discharged by the RMO following the tribunal.

In a limited way, adjournments provided some members with a means of rectifying what they saw as injustices within a therapeutic system that they could not otherwise influence.

Summary

Presidents play a central role in balancing the needs of the different participants in the tribunal and ensuring that the tribunal is fair. They were conscious of the need, while establishing the evidence, to protect the relationship between the patient and his or her RMO and between the patient and his or her family. Patients were dealt with sensitively and there were relatively few tribunals in which patients became emotional or stressed by the ordeal.

In different regions there appeared to be different policies regarding whether the patient was heard first or last, and equally persuasive arguments were advanced for both courses of action. The RMO was observed to be present for longer in those tribunals in which the patient's evidence was heard first.

The nature and type of evidence presented at a tribunal is both complex and difficult to verify. In the majority of tribunals the key pieces of evidence routinely sought by members were the presence or absence of symptoms and, in particular, insight, whether the patient was cooperating with treatment and the risk and danger of the patient to other people. In many tribunals, the reports and information provided by witnesses were found to be inadequate and divergent, leaving tribunal members frequently unable to decide whose version of events was the most accurate.

Notes

1 Eldergill (1998, p. 810) suggests that 'if the patient does not attend the tribunal, the tribunal must ascertain the reasons for that and should offer him an interview in private with them. They should consider the need to adjourn the proceedings *sine die*.' He ends by saying that the tribunal has a discretion to proceed in the applicant's absence where he declines to attend but their discretion must not be abused.

2 Not her real name.

3 RMO unable to attend so SHO (senior house officer) attended on RMO's behalf having consulted with RMO prior to tribunal.

4 Pt = patient.

5 The Mental Health Review Tribunal Panel, established by the Law Society, requires members to fulfil certain membership conditions, such as the attendance on an approved course, at a minimum of four tribunals and at an interview. Legal aid representation is limited to legal practices specifically approved for this purpose by the Legal Services Commission. The latest figures suggest that there are currently only 43 legal practices across England and Wales which have a franchise to offer legal representation services to a patient appearing before an MHRT.

6 Under the Rules (rule 12), suitably qualified professional people have access to documents from which family and friends are excluded.

7
The Deliberation

Once the evidence has been heard during the hearing, the witnesses withdraw and the tribunal members deliberate *in camera*. Very little is prescribed about the conduct of the deliberation, other than that the tribunal president should ensure that each member has an equal voice in the decision-making and contributes to the Statement of Reasons. In this chapter, we examine the process by which decisions were made. This includes the way in which the deliberation was conducted, who spoke, and how tribunal members used the information with which they were presented. In the next chapter we examine the content of the discussion in relation to decisions about the statutory criteria.

The process

From studies of juror decision-making, it is known that different jurors can draw different conclusions about the right verdict, despite being faced with exactly the same evidence (Ellsworth, 1993). The task facing tribunal members is similar to that of jurors. It could be argued that, as a result of the informality of the tribunal process, members are less constrained than juries by rules of evidence, statutes and legal conventions. Nevertheless, they are faced with a substantial volume of information, written and oral, objective and subjective, consistent and divergent, often produced in cramped and highly charged circumstances.

Tribunals have clearly defined stages, each with a specific purpose. We had therefore assumed, before our observations, that tribunals would exemplify the circumstances under which professional decision-making would be at its most explicit. We had also assumed that the discussions between the three members, at the end of the hearing, would draw out the similarities and differences between members in the interpretation and weighting of the evidence. We believed that our observations would elicit the interpretative framework within which each member was working. These assumptions proved unfounded. There were wide variations in the style, content and dynamics of decision-making, which rendered impossible the development of a neat and authentic typology of decision-making. We have, therefore, identified the key dimensions along which variations occurred.

The task

Tribunal members have a well-defined task. They are charged with making decisions about discharge according to predefined criteria. As previously stated, the powers to discharge a patient derive from s. 72 of the MHA 1983:

> (1) Where application is made to a Mental Health Review Tribunal by or in respect of a patient who is liable to be detained under this Act, the tribunal may in any case direct that the patient be discharged, and –
> (a) the tribunal shall direct the discharge of a patient liable to be detained under section 2 above if they are satisfied –
> (i) that he is not then suffering from mental disorder or from mental disorder of a nature or degree which warrants his detention in hospital for assessment (or for assessment followed by a medical treatment) for at least a limited period; or
> (ii) that his detention as aforesaid is not justified in the interests of his own health or safety or with a view to the protection of other persons;
> (b) the tribunal shall direct the discharge of a patient liable to be detained otherwise than under section 2 above if they are satisfied –
> (i) that he is not then suffering from mental illness, psychopathic disorder, severe mental impairment or mental impairment or from any of those forms of disorder of a nature or degree which makes it appropriate for him to be detained in a hospital for medical treatment; or
> (ii) that it is not necessary for the health or safety of the patient or for the protection of other persons that he should receive such treatment; or
> (iii) in the case of an application by virtue of paragraph (g) of section 66(1) above, that the patient, if released, would not be likely to act in a manner dangerous to other persons or to himself.
> (2) In determining whether to direct the discharge of a patient detained otherwise than under section 2 above in a case not falling within paragraph (b) of subsection (1) above, the tribunal shall have regard –
> (a) to the likelihood of medical treatment alleviating or preventing a deterioration of the patient's condition; and
> (b) in the case of a patient suffering from mental illness or severe mental impairment, to the likelihood of the patient, if discharged, being able to care for himself, to obtain the care he needs or to guard himself against serious exploitation.

The *Guide for Members* states 'the tribunal will endeavour to reach each decision by discussion and by consensus. The decision of the tribunal is that of the majority; where (unusually) four members are sitting and equal votes are cast the president has a casting vote, but otherwise has an equal voice with the other two members' (1996b, p. 10). To assist them, members have access to rules of procedure laid out in the Mental Health Review Tribunal Rules 1983 (SI 1983

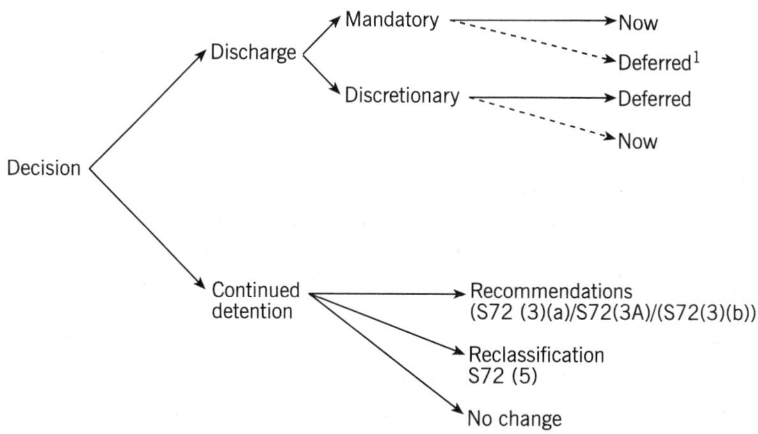

Figure 7.1

No. 942). The Rules are also laid out in the *Guide for Members*. Members are kept up-to-date with the outcomes when tribunal decisions have been judicially reviewed.

Tribunals have essentially two choices – to discharge or not to discharge. Once they have made a decision in relation to discharge they can consider whether to defer discharge and whether to make recommendations (see Figure 7.1).

The amount and type of discussion in reaching a decision

In over a third of the observed tribunals, the decision was reached and written up in ten minutes or less. Indeed, in over two-thirds of cases both activities were completed within 15 minutes (see Table 7.1).

Table 7.1 shows that, between and within regions, there were variations in the length of time taken to reach and record decisions.

It is important to track how decisions were reached, to elicit whether due consideration can be said to have been given to the evidence and whether the evidence was considered in relation to the statutory criteria. There were three types of exchange during deliberations:

Table 7.1 *Duration of deliberations, including the writing of the decisions*

No. of tribunals

Deliberation (Duration in minutes)	Region 1	Region 2	Region 3	Region 4	Total
5 minutes or less	4	5	1	6	16
6–10 minutes	–	4	3	1	8
11–15 minutes	3	2	7	5	17
16–20 minutes	3	3	1	2	9
21–40 minutes	3	2	3	1	9
41+ minutes	2	–	–	–	2
Total	15	16	15	15	61

(i) no discussion;
(ii) structured discussion; and
(iii) unstructured discussion.

(i) No discussion

In 11 deliberations there was no significant exchange of views. The deliberations took less than 5 minutes. This absence of significant discussion is illustrated in the following unabridged, verbatim reports of the full discussion:

Pres ➜ *It's fairly clear we can't discharge.*
LM ➜ *We approve plans of the RMO and SW.*
*(*The president then begins writing the decision.*)* (RB13)
Pres ➜ *What do you think?*
LM ➜ *He fulfils the criteria.*
MM ➜ *No change.*
*(*The president then begins writing the decision.*)* (RB09)

As can be seen, only two members were involved in each discussion and the interaction was confined to one member agreeing to the other member's proposed course of action. The writing of the decision then began.

In some tribunals in this category, the statutory criteria were briefly addressed:

Pres ➜ *Mental disorder?*
MM ➜ *Mental illness of both nature and degree and it is health and safety.*
Pres ➜ *She definitely needs to stay in. (*turns to LM*)*
LM ➜ *Mmm. (*nods head in agreement*)*
*(*The president then begins writing the decision.*)* (RD02)

Pres ➜ *Should we consider if he meets the statutory criteria?*
MM ➜ *Yes.*
Pres ➜ *Health or safety?*
LM ➜ *I think all three.*
MM ➜ *I think the worst risk is that he would end up in the criminal justice system.*
Pres ➜ *Let me read you what I have written.* (RB06)

Logically, the development of reasons should precede the decision for which they are reasons. In tribunals, the reasons should be a product of the interactions of all three members. However, in two instances the deliberation began with the president writing the decision without any reference to the other members. Consensus appeared to have been reached by osmosis, without any attempt to identify whether there were shared or divergent interpretations of the evidence. As the writing of the decision occurred without prior discussion, it appears that in each case the president had arrived at reasons and a decision during the course of the hearing. The writing of the decision without consultation seems to have been based on the assumption that there were no other possible outcomes and that, consequently, the other members would have shared the decision had they been consulted. Presumably had the other members disagreed a discussion would have ensued.

The non-participating members did not, in either case, appear concerned or surprised at their lack of involvement. It is possible that the decision was so clear-cut that members did not feel the need to discuss the outcome. It is also possible that members were used to the fact that not all members participated in decision-making.

(ii) Structured discussion

In just over half of all tribunals, a fairly structured 'discussion' took place under the leadership or guidance of one member. With a few exceptions, they were initiated and managed by the president. In a couple of tribunals less experienced presidents invited the medical members to structure the discussion:

> *I suppose you do have a checklist in your mind, the fundamentals are always the same. One has always got to bear in mind the legal test, whether they've got an illness and whether it's of sufficient severity for them to be liable to detention, so you've always got to be testing everything against the actual criteria in the sections all the time.* (Pres 14)

In the tribunals we observed, the discussion was structured around the decision or outcome. The president would commonly seek answers to a general question such as that below, or to a specific set of questions usually grounded in the statutory criteria:

> *Pres* ➔ *Anyone reject the RMO proposition that patient has an underlying mental illness?* (RB14)
> *Pres* ➔ *Are we satisfied that she has a mental impairment?*
> (All nod in agreement.)
> *Pres* ➔ *And that she requires detention?*
> *MM* ➔ *Yes.*
> *LM* ➔ *Mmm.*
> *Pres* ➔ *And that she would stop medication and risk her own health?*
> *MM* ➔ *Yes.*
> *LM* ➔ *Yes.* (RC09)

When the statutory criteria were explicitly used to structure the questioning, questions were either posed to each tribunal member in turn or were raised by the president in the expectation that someone would answer. Whether or not discussion flowed from these questions or statements depended on the other tribunal members.

The interviews confirmed that, for some presidents, this structuring of information around outcomes was a conscious and routine strategy, which was considered to deliver good decision-making. Although it was a way of ensuring that each member had a say in the final decision, it supported only a partial analysis of the evidence since only evidence considered relevant to the decision was discussed.

> *Pres* ➔ *We have to base our decision on the evidence – we have to ignore our emotions. Maybe I am being too legislative but we have to base our action on the evidence. Once we go beyond that we are basing our actions on inadequate evidence.* (RA11)

In some cases in this category, the proceedings were truncated by presidents, who controlled the discussion by restricting rather than facilitating discussion. This appeared to be underpinned by the idea that members should each arrive separately at their decision, with discussion required only if agreement could not be reached.

(iii) Unstructured discussion

Approximately a third of all tribunal deliberations were characterised by informal and unstructured discussions. Information was discussed in an ad hoc way, with no detectable logic in the way in which subjects were introduced or omitted, and topics, when raised, were rarely explored fully.

The major topics were usually those that were considered by members to be important or pertinent. Retrospective analysis showed that a topic could be reopened many times without much progress being made in terms of understanding, agreement or resolution. In all but a few tribunals, this lack of structure resulted in a partial and incomplete review of the evidence.

In this category, tribunals seemed to be most influenced by the personalities of the individual members, the group dynamics that developed, and the nature of the patient's case.

In the following extract we present the entire deliberation which was typical of unstructured discussions.

> *Pres* ➔ *What do we think? (*turning to MM*)*
> *MM* ➔ *I have questions about diagnosis and in particular his history. Both parents are schizophrenic, so we have to give him the benefit of the doubt. He is suffering from schizophrenic illness. He has had delusions and heard voices. He is paranoid and doesn't trust anyone. Taking all that on board and his present circumstances, the problem requires long-term detention for treatment. The question remains as to whether he will allow it. He has never had consistent treatment on a long-term basis.*
> *LM* ➔ *I agree he needs to be in hospital. He needs consistency.*
> *MM* ➔ *He was not making a case to be discharged. I don't understand why. The question of his IQ is a very important one in relation to his treatment.*
> *LM* ➔ *Yes, the nurses need to work at his level.*
> *Clerk* ➔ *He needs a psychological assessment.*

Pres ➜ Yes, as discussed before. So you're both of the view that he is ill of a nature and degree. He lacks insight. If not under section he won't take his medication which is detrimental to his own health. There is no evidence that he has actually tried to harm himself, but it's detrimental to his own health. (The president then begins writing the decision.) (RA12)

Discussions in this category often began with a direct emotional response to the evidence. Some cases were extremely distressing and members seemed to need to express their reactions before they could move on to discuss the case.

MM ➜ Poor thing.
Pres ➜ How very sad. It's not often I feel so sorry for people.
MM ➜ I had a good talk with her before and she doesn't like it here.
Pres ➜ Her parents don't want her.
MM ➜ They don't want her at home. (RB02)

The problem with this type of discussion became apparent through retrospective analysis. The discussions were not efficient. Members failed to focus on issues, explore them, reach agreement, and then move on. Issues repeatedly bubbled along throughout the discussion, rising to the surface, sinking and then resurfacing. Decisions appeared to emerge from an evidential soup without it ever being clear on what they were based.

The nature of the cases

Perhaps not surprisingly, the nature of the case was the single biggest determinant of the volume of discussion. All respondents described in the interviews a distinction between cases they described as 'clear-cut' in nature and those which were 'borderline'. In the observed tribunals 'borderline' cases resulted in more lengthy discussions than did clear-cut cases.

I mean you get borderline cases. There was a section 2 case which I did, where the patient had been in hospital for about 14 days and there was a clear diagnosis of schizophrenia so the nature of the illness wasn't really in dispute, but the degree was very iffy because there was a suggestion from the RMO that this patient was probably just about ready for discharge, within a day or two. The question was whether they were still liable for detention, so we really had to wrestle then with what we were being told, what the patient was saying, what our own medical member was saying ... Sometimes you feel that it's pretty clear-cut and there's no way that they're ready or it's clear that they are. (Pres 14)

In adopting the categories 'clear-cut' and 'borderline' we are reflecting members' views of the cases they heard. In this section we will explore what this distinction involved.

Clear-cut cases

In most 'clear-cut' tribunals the decision appeared to be straightforward, concerning patients elsewhere described as 'hopeless and helpless' (Peay, 1989). These were tribunals characterised by agreement and certainty about the need or otherwise for continued detention. The evidence that formed the basis of this decision was not made explicit; in 11 of the tribunals we observed in this category there was no discussion at all. The following is an extract from one such tribunal:

> *MM* ➜ *No question.*
> *Pres* ➜ *Fulfils the criteria.*
> *MM* ➜ *Yes.* (RD07)

This absence of discussion makes it difficult to draw any conclusions about the factors which made a case so clear-cut. There were some clear-cut cases in which there was a limited amount of discussion. These discussions were mainly of the structured type and were outcome driven. It appeared, however, in these cases that the outcome was decided early and by consensus, and the discussion which followed involved selecting the evidence to support the decision. Any evidence brought out in the hearing that did not support the outcome was left out. The decision therefore appeared straightforward:

> *I mean quite often the decision is quite easy because we've all reached the same conclusion independently, and we just sit down and I say, 'does anyone want to discharge this patient?' The answer is no, and we're all agreed, and that's it. We needn't discuss anything further. We then discuss what the reasons are.* (Pres 02)

While this might explain why some cases were easily decided, it does not provide the whole explanation. Clear-cut cases were generally those cases where patients demonstrated clear evidence of symptoms during the hearing, where the evidence of the RMO was confirmed by the patient, and high risks were perceived to be associated with any course of action other than continued detention. In other words, in the minds of the members, the patient did not satisfy the discharge criteria:

> *LM* ➜ *She is ill within the meaning of the Act. There is a lot of evidence that she will harm herself.*
> *MM* ➜ *We can pick up on that in the reasons for keeping section on.*
> *(*The president then begins writing the decision on the form.*)* (RC08)

All the clear-cut cases observed were cases resulting in a decision in favour of continued detention. While there is, at least in theory, the possibility of clear-cut cases resulting in discharge, in reality, the five patients discharged in this study were all classified as 'borderline'.

Presenting only the evidence that proves the hypothesis is a phenomenon that receives considerable attention in the psychology of criminal evidence. Some authors suggest (Wagenaar *et al.*, 1993) that, in adopting this method of decision-making, the real problem is not the order but the way in which the selection of the evidence remains undocumented and unexplained. We return to this issue later when we examine the strategies that members used to select evidence.

Borderline cases

A significant minority of cases were considered to be 'borderline'. They included all the cases in which patients were discharged:

> *Pres* ➜ *I'm ambivalent – we all are – I am with XX (*the medical member*), just – okay then.* (RD09)

These cases were characterised by uncertainty, and discussion was generally driven by the lack of consensus on a number of evidential fronts. These were:

- *Clinical* – the absence of symptoms, either not exhibited during the hearing or contradictory reporting of symptoms; disputed accounts of insight and/or compliance.
- *Evidential* – competing and disputed interpretations of events.
- *Behavioural* – doubts about the association of behaviour with mental disorder.
- *Risk* – uncertainty over the degree of risk posed by the patient if released from section.

Differences of opinion did occur in borderline cases but opinions were not strongly held. In part this was facilitated by the uncertainty arising from divergent accounts. Several members also commented in the interviews on the way that the level of rapport or understanding between them facilitated a consensual approach to decision-making. It appeared as if all members operated within the same framework, described by some as a 'common-sense approach':

> *When members become experienced then they've all got a jolly good idea about what mental disorder is about, so really they all see it from the same point of view.* (MM10)

> *Disagreements are relatively few and far between, and always resolved. (Pres 02)*

> *We are on the same wavelength. We know what we think about it all and therefore we are not liable to disagree.* (MM06)

From the researcher's point of view, differences of opinion were important because they required members to be more than usually explicit about why they held their views.

Divergence was ultimately about the final decision – whether or not to discharge. But divergence was rarely in the first instance about outcome.

Disagreement most often emerged in relation to an interpretation of a piece of information.

> *MM* ➔ *If he has no insight, it is rational for him to object to being here.*
> *LM* ➔ *You can't fault this patient on that, you can't say he has no insight.* (Someone enters the room and goes out again.)
> *LM* ➔ *He has to me given a perfectly satisfactory explanation for his behaviour. If I were in his place I might be the same. He's satisfied me. The hospital is not serving any purpose.*
> *MM* ➔ *He won't come back. He drinks like a fish.*
> *LM* ➔ *What separates us is this – You believe he would not take his medication and I believe he would.*
> *MM* ➔ *Why did he tell me he wouldn't?*
> *LM* ➔ *I accept all that, but he presented very well. What is influencing me is that the hospital is bad for him. I am taking the line of discretionary discharge almost.*
> *Pres* ➔ *We need to satisfy the legal criteria first.*
> *LM* ➔ *I am agreed on there being a disorder.*
> *MM* ➔ *It's a question of degree.*
> *Pres* ➔ *The patient is unpredictable, fluctuating and unstable.*
> *LM* ➔ *He is not violent.*
> *MM* ➔ *Just drunk and disorderly.*
> *LM* ➔ *That doesn't make him violent, just a nuisance, he's frightened.*
> *Pres* ➔ *The social worker says his fears, are unusual.*
> *MM* ➔ *So, is it only in the interests of his own health to keep the section on?*
> *Pres* ➔ *I don't agree, there is enough evidence of risk. He might be unsafe.*
> *MM* ➔ *You could say that of any schizophrenic.*
> *Pres* ➔ *Who's for discharge?*
> *LM* ➔ *I am not going to press for it if it's my decision alone. I won't push it, as I know the line you two are on. I'll happily go along with your decision.* (RD15)

Although this is an example of disagreement, the two members do not move beyond stating their views. Neither party seemed willing to unpick the evidence on any of the issues being addressed.

As this example demonstrates, when there were differences of opinion over discharge, they generally seemed to be resolved easily and amicably – with the dissenter either agreeing to differ or being persuaded to go with the majority. Opinions did not often appear to be held very strongly, particularly among presidents and lay members.

One of the most interesting examples of disagreements involved a medical member who argued for the release of a patient and, unusually, strongly voiced this at the outset. The medical member's view was that the patient was able to come and go from the hospital as he pleased and it was unclear why the RMO had not discharged him:

Pres ➜ *He is thought disordered, isn't he?*
MM ➜ *Thought disorder in itself is not a reason to detain. If I now ask myself, nature or degree, I have to say 'No'. You can't keep him on a section just to treat him in the community. It is against the spirit of the Act.*
Pres ➜ *It [his condition] is too fragile to discharge.*
MM ➜ *In the reasons we have to say that he suffers from mental illness, the evidence of which is?*
Pres ➜ *For a considerable time he suffered a serious psychotic illness which responded to treatment in hospital and the symptoms are now largely controlled.*
MM ➜ *But not currently of a degree which makes him liable to be detained.*
Pres ➜ *What about risk of relapse?*
MM ➜ *It is pragmatic what you are suggesting, but it is not lawful. If you follow your argument everyone with schizophrenia would be detained... We are contemplating a significant injustice.*
Pres ➜ *(*turning to the lay member*) You have the casting vote.*
LM ➜ *Well, if it satisfies the legality of it he should stay.*
Pres ➜ *It satisfies because of what I think. It's not a legal point. It's factual.*
LM ➜ *My vote comes down for him to stay.*
Pres ➜ *It's very unusual a split decision.*
LM ➜ *If it's a real problem I... (*interrupted by medical member*).*
MM ➜ *It's no problem at all to me – I don't see what else we can do.*
*(*pause while they both look at the president writing in his book*)*
MM ➜ *The solicitor is not on the list so there won't be a judicial review.* (RB05)

Wood (1970), in recognising the importance of the medical member's prior examination of the patient, states that 'clearly the results of this examination are crucial, for a tribunal is bound to rely heavily upon the medical opinion of the doctor'. He goes on to say 'it will be an unusual tribunal which discharges a patient or makes a recommendation to the Home Secretary contrary to the medical member's advice'.

One of the interesting aspects of the above account is that the tribunal president and lay member opted to detain the patient against the advice of the medical member on the basis of their interpretation of the clinical picture. Another important point, to be discussed later, arises from the medical member's last comment of the preceding quote (RB05). The list to which the medical member refers is the Law Society's panel of solicitors and their employees with expertise on advising and representing patients detained under the Mental Health Act 1983. Solicitors, legal executives, trainee solicitors and solicitors' clerks who have attended a compulsory training course and can satisfy specific experience and knowledge criteria may apply for membership to the panel. The medical member suggests that the patient's legal representative may not be as familiar with mental health legislation as an accredited panel member and therefore that the decision made by the tribunal will not be subject to judicial review. Judicial review being the means by which the tribunal's proceedings may be challenged[2].

Key issues in the decision-making process and strategies for dealing with them

Unresolved questions and missing information

When we analysed the tribunal transcripts, we often found it difficult to come to conclusions about events described in the reports and discussed in the hearing because discrepancies or divergences of accounts were not resolved. In addition, missing information was either accepted as such by the tribunal members or hypothesis or conjecture were substituted for the information that was missing.

In one tribunal in which the patient was discharged, the medical member asks the president in the deliberation:

MM ➜ *Is it useful to say what evidence we could have seen?*
Pres ➜ *Well it would have been useful to see his sister, some family thing has gone on there.* (RD09)

Acceptance of missing information by tribunal members was not always as passive as demonstrated by the above quote. In some deliberations there were concerted attempts by members to work out the importance of the missing information and how the information gap could be filled. In the main (and with the exception of adjourned tribunals) members lived with gaps in the information:

MM ➜ *We don't know the extent of her delusions, nor how she copes at night. Do you think it matters? Probably not.* (RA02)

Pres (to medical member) ➜ *Do you think he will take his medication?*
MM ➜ *No. He didn't before.*
Pres ➜ *He says he would.*
MM ➜ *I don't believe him.* (RD03)

The substitution of hypothesis or conjecture for missing information appeared to occur at a relatively low level. And yet, the implications were potentially quite important:

LM ➜ *How does the patient motivate herself to get to the clinic to have her blood test done?*
MM ➜ *Her key worker probably takes her.* (RD01)

LM ➜ *How is he taking drugs?*
MM ➜ *I think he is getting cannabis on the ward and the RMO underestimates the effect of cannabis use on his schizophrenia.* (RD07)

MM ➜ *I wanted to ask him [RMO] if he'd changed his mind since he wrote that [last report] but I forgot.* (RD11)

Discrepancies in evidence

The volume of evidence, and the way in which it is presented and elicited in tribunal hearings, make it very difficult for all but the most rudimentary forms of decision-making in the time available. In the vast majority of cases, decisions over evidence were not considered in a robust way. Discrepancies in evidence presented the biggest challenge to members. Rather than sifting evidence, or assessing the plausibility of the different narratives provided by the witnesses, members usually considered the credibility of each witness in a global sense. This was particularly the case where the patient said one thing and the professionals another; or where there were two different reports of the same event:

> *A lot of it is gut feeling as to whether or not it's in the interests of the patient or the public whether they should be released. It's bound to be, isn't it, based on the evidence which you've heard. Whether or not the patient is telling the truth.* (Pres 13)

Some members recognised the complexity of deciding where the truth lay. They were quick to point out that, with mental illness, what was under discussion was frequently a matter of interpretation and opinion.

> *The procedure isn't terribly well adapted I suspect, a doctor, a lawyer and a lay person reaching a decision about what is fact and what isn't.* (Pres 07)

Identifying the version of events which best added up was frequently a matter of establishing a credible narrative and identifying credible witnesses.

Credible narrative

Establishing a credible narrative involved identifying whether there was another interpretation for a patient's behaviour, for example, 'Is a patient's paranoia a result of their mental illness or is it possible that the patient is actually being persecuted by their neighbours?' In many cases, attempts to establish whether there were alternative explanations were complicated by lack of evidence. Lines of enquiry simply could not deliver irrefutable evidence one way or another.

In interview, some members recalled tribunals in which conflicts of evidence had been resolved almost by chance. One president (Pres 08) described a tribunal in which an RMO alleged that his patient had been living in a state of extreme neglect. The RMO in making this allegation was relying on reports in the patient's case notes. The patient denied that there were any problems with his living conditions. Something about the patient's defence of his living conditions encouraged the president to pursue the issue. As the complexity of the divergent views unfolded, the president became more convinced that the two accounts did 'not add up'. The patient's community psychiatric nurse (CPN) who happened to be in the hospital was summoned to the tribunal. The CPN had seen the flat recently and confirmed that, although on a previous admission to the hospital the patient's flat had indeed been chaotic and untidy, before his recent admission this had not been the case. In this instance the discrepancy between the two accounts was resolved by tangible evidence and an account which made sense of both the RMO's views and those of the patient. In other instances, where tangible evidence was not forthcoming, tribunal members recognised the value of hearing the same evidence from a number of different sources.

> *Some of what you hear from the RMO and the nursing staff is backed up by hearing it more than once, so it's sort of corroborated if you like, in legal terms, and so you can give more weight I suppose to that evidence because you've heard it from a number of different sources.* (Pres 14)

In the interviews, however, some members reported a wariness of written evidence, feeling that factual inaccuracies could creep in, often as a result of the circumstances under which the patient was admitted:

> *Very often – you'll find that when somebody's been brought into hospital after some kind of critical episode, the facts of that episode are very unclear and there's been a kind of process of Chinese whispers, and that what comes over in the report is quite different from what appears in the original record in the notes.* (LM 14)

The *Annual Report of the Council on Tribunals* (1983)[3] expressed concern about the inclusion in reports of unsubstantiated statements prefixed by 'the charge nurse reports' or 'a member of staff alleges'. However, in the main but not exclusively, reports from the professionals providing care to the patient seemed in practice to be accepted at face value. There were a number of deliberations in which members believed the patient posed a risk, based on an assumption that uncorroborated and vague allegations of offending were true.

Surprisingly, a minority of the presidents interviewed expressed a belief that conflicts of evidence did not exist:

> *We never get conflicts of actual evidence. It's a question of opinion as to the condition of the patient. Occasionally the patient denies something or puts a spin on it – I think that's the term that everyone uses these days. It's fairly easy to go behind that.* (Pres 13)

When much of what is being discussed depends on 'opinion' it is not surprising that extensive use was made of the 'credible witness'.

Credible witnesses

> *LM* ➔ *We are here to decide who to believe.* (RA07)

> *You have to work out who you think is telling the truth and be careful about hearsay evidence.* (LM19)

In trying to assess the weight of the evidence with which they were presented, it was clear from the observations that members often adopted a short-cut technique of assessing whether the witness was credible or had an ulterior motive. Once this had been decided, that person's information tended to be treated as credible or suspect depending on the assessment of motive.

In the interviews there was a commonly held belief that RMOs had no reason to lie or detain patients unnecessarily. Such was the pressure on beds that members believed RMOs were more likely to try to 'get people better and out of hospital' than keep them in unnecessarily.

> *Pres ➜ I am encouraged by the evidence of the RMO. She is not in the business of keeping him inside without offering anything.*
> *LM ➜ I am sure she may think that she can do something. She's got to have hope.*
> *MM ➜ It's irredeemable in my view.* (RB12)

Members nearly always subjected evidence from patients to a greater level of questioning, which, through the effects of mental illness and the patient's desire to be discharged was felt less likely to be reliable. Particular questions were raised about whether the person could be trusted to maintain good progress without clinical supervision and social control:

> *So the big problem is assessing whether or not you can trust them when they say 'I will stay voluntarily' or 'I will come in' or whatever. And that probably is the most difficult bit.* (LM19)

Problems were created on the rare occasion that a patient was seen to present as a credible witness. This was largely because according the patient credibility raised the possibility that the patient might meet the criteria for discharge.

> *Pres ➜ The patient spoke up well. I am persuaded that he has accepted his illness and will cooperate.* (RD15)

It was, however, much more common for the patient's evidence to be disbelieved and, as described in the pre-hearing meeting, the medical member might already have provided a framework within which to interpret the patient's evidence:

> *MM ➜ Not as straightforward as she'd like you to believe* (RD01)
> *Pres ➜ Is he telling the truth?* (RD11)
> *MM ➜ Easy to be blinded by articulacy. She is very bright … She is mentally disordered, but not based on having heard her, from her records.* (RD08)
> *MM ➜ She is bright. She knows what to say.* (RD14)
> *MM ➜ It depends on whether we can rely on her carrying her promises, although on presentation today I am not convinced.* (RA01)
> *MM ➜ I have no faith in his statement that he will stay in hospital.* (RA04)
> *LM ➜ There's obviously a lot more to it than she said.* (RA07)

Pres ➜ *I find it difficult – part of me says he is a con merchant.* (RA08)
Pres ➜ *I think the patient presented well because he has learned the drill, not because he has improved. The RMO is unable to elicit symptoms but with father's evidence I am absolutely sure he suffers from a mental disorder that requires further assessment.* (RA10)
MM ➜ *The patient knows he has to say that to maximise his chances of getting out. What he says, he would say that anyway – he has heard two years – if he begins to cooperate he is signing his own prison term.* (RB12)

The patient's family and friends were usually considered to be 'on the patient's side', although this was not always the case. Their evidence was therefore usually given less weight than that of the clinicians:

LM ➜ *The patient's friend was mad.*
Pres ➜ *What about his girlfriend?*
MM ➜ *I didn't believe the patient's girlfriend – silly ass!* (RD09)
Pres ➜ *Mum is making it up.* (RC10)

The extent to which professionals were thought to be credible sometimes depended on their performance on the day. The benchmark by which tribunal members assessed a professional's evidence as useful and believable related to their knowledge of the patient's history, current mental state, and response to treatment; and, in the case of social workers, knowledge of social circumstances and the availability of future community-based options:

Pres ➜ *What a social worker! Wasn't he awful! Didn't know anything!* (RB01)
LM ➜ *I don't like the social worker. I believe the nurse re the presence of delusions.* (RC01)
Pres ➜ *The nurse was brilliant. Without her we'd have had a much more difficult job.* (RC08)

In some respects the process of identifying credible witnesses elucidated which evidence was considered:

Pres ➜ *I am relying on the evidence of the father, doctor and social worker. The nurse's evidence was not any good.* (RA15)

Considering discretion

The tribunal has a general discretion to discharge, even if it decides that the statutory criteria for discharge are not met. At the end of their submission, legal representatives normally reminded tribunal members of this discretion. We did not observe any cases where discretion was used to discharge. On a few occasions during the deliberation the president raised the tribunal's power of discretion only to dismiss its use immediately afterwards without any discussion.

All members were asked in the interview in what circumstances they would use their discretionary power to discharge. Most of them admitted that they had no idea. A few presidents were able to recall circumstances in which they had used it:

> *I've used it on a couple of occasions. It's really occasions where you accept that a patient is ill, but you're not sure that they're actually gaining anything by remaining in hospital.* (Pres 08)

Summary

Tribunal deliberations varied enormously in length. In over a third of the observed tribunals, the decision was reached and written up in ten minutes or less. Indeed, in over two-thirds of cases both activities were completed within 15 minutes. As we have demonstrated, in some deliberations there was no discussion at all between the members before the president started writing the Statement of Reasons.

Where there was discussion, this was either structured and managed by one member of the tribunal, usually the president or it was unstructured. Unstructured discussions meandered around in an ad hoc way and topics, when raised, were rarely fully explored. In the majority of tribunals the medical member played an influential role in the way in which a decision was reached – being important in both the definition of mental disorder and the nature of risk posed by the patient.

Members used short cuts to enable them to sift through the volume of evidence that they had heard. Although some cases were 'clear-cut', others were more complex and in the minds of the tribunal members 'borderline'. Identifying credible narratives and credible witnesses enabled tribunal members to maintain the integrity of evidence and come to swift assessments of the evidence they had heard.

Notes

1 There are differences of opinion as to whether it is legal to defer the discharge of a patient who meets the statutory criteria for discharge. Rutherford QC writing in the MHRT *Members' News Sheet* (Issue 15, June 1995) suggests that it is possible to interpret s. 72(3) in a number of ways. She states that provided the power to defer is used properly and lawfully, that is deferring the discharge only for very good reasons 'such as the preparation/provision of accommodation and for the shortest possible time, and where it is in the Tribunal's collective professional opinion that it is entirely in the interests of the patient and within the spirit of the Act which is to protect the liberty of the individual' and not to 'see whether the patient gets any worse/better', then the provision can be applied to both a mandatory and a discretionary discharge. According to Eldergill (1998) the paramount rule of statutory construction that 'every statute is to be expounded according to its manifest and

expressed intention' applies in this case, clearly showing the importance of postponing discharge where arrangements need to be put in place.

2 Eldergill (1998) states that the High Court will only get involved if the tribunal's decision was defective because it acted unlawfully, irrationally, or improperly. Eldergill also adds that almost all successful applications concern a tribunal exceeding its jurisdiction or failing to give adequate and proper reasons for its decision.

3 The Council on Tribunals is established under the Tribunal and Inquiries Act 1992, and is required to keep under review the constitution and workings of MHRTs (s.1(1)(a), Sced. 1).

8

The Statutory Criteria for Discharge

The last chapter showed the variety of ways in which decision-making took place by tribunal members. The detailed content of discussions depended on the precise nature of each case. In this chapter, we examine how members interpreted the statutory criteria when making decisions about discharge from sections 2 and 3 of the Mental Health Act (MHA) 1983.

The statutory criteria

At first sight, the statutory criteria[1] seem to provide a clear framework for decision-making. But, dig a little deeper and the full complexities are exposed. Members' approach to evidence was not unconnected with their difficulties in understanding and interpreting the statutory criteria. A detailed analysis of the observational and interview data suggests that members were familiar with the language of the MHA 1983 but did not always know how to interpret the criteria or apply them to the evidence. They developed a broad-brush approach that blurred the fine detail of the Act, replacing it with their own impression of the Act's intentions:

> *I don't think the rules are sufficiently clearly drawn. If* (hesitates) *– in theory I suppose, you would say, 'here we have rules which set out you shall do something in defined circumstances, and I therefore, as a lawyer, am there to interpret those rules to the tribunal, and as chairman, to ensure that this is what is done'. In practice it seems to me that the rules themselves are sufficiently loose, or loosely drawn, that the facts we find affect the way the rule operates. And that it's our finding of the facts that actually determines the decision, and not the framing of the rules. And it's in this way that I'm saying that in essence it seems to me that it simply is a way of exercising discretion.* (Pres 02)

The MHA 1983 defines four classes of mental disorder: mental illness, severe mental impairment, mental impairment, and psychopathic disorder. Mental illness has no statutory definition. Severe mental impairment and mental impairment differ only in degree and relate to a state of arrested or incomplete development of mind. Psychopathic disorder means a persistent disorder or disability of the mind, whether or not including significant impairment of intelligence, which results in abnormally aggressive or irresponsible conduct. Classifications are not watertight, with clinicians differing in their interpretation of the finer points.

In 1997–98, most patients admitted to NHS hospitals, and detained under Part II of the MHA 1983, were classified as suffering from mental illness (Department of Health, 1998). With few exceptions, patients in this study had been classified as mentally ill and therefore much of the following discussion relates to mental illness.

The conditions covered by mental illness include schizophrenia and mood disorders. Mental illness is not statutorily defined, but the MHA 1983 does provide that no person may be treated as suffering from mental illness by reason only of promiscuity or other immoral conduct, sexual deviancy or dependence on alcohol or drugs.

The term mental illness was not defined when introduced into the Mental Treatment Act 1930 (MTA 1930). Subsequent attempts to define mental illness have highlighted the difficulties of arriving at a satisfactory definition that would, in the words of some commentators, stand the test of time. According to the interdepartmental committee, established in 1975 to review the MHA 1959[2], there had not been much evidence that the lack of a definition had led to particular problems. In line with this, the Department of Health's view, in framing the MHA 1983, was that the term's operational definition and usage should remain a matter for clinical judgement.

The courts have been largely reluctant to attempt to define mental illness. However, in 1974, Lord Justice Lawton[3] ruled in the Court of Appeal that the words mental illness are 'ordinary words' of the English language:

> *They have no particular medical significance. They have no particular legal significance. How should the Courts construe them? … in a way that ordinary sensible people would construe them.*

Perhaps not surprisingly, Lord Justice Lawton's view that mental illness has neither legal nor medical significance is considered by many to be unsustainable (see Eldergill, 1998, pp. 65–6). The legal debate was moved on in 1985 by Lord Justice Ackner[4] who, in recognising the limitations of the ordinary lay person in diagnosing mental illness, highlighted the importance of the lay opinion in the tribunal as a basis against which medical opinion may be tested.

The MHA 1959 introduced the terms 'nature' and 'degree' in order to define the severity of disorder necessary to qualify as 'mental disorder'. However, they stand as two separate tests and are not interchangeable:

> *The term 'mental illness' is not defined. Its interpretation is a matter for medical judgement, but it is expected that when it is qualified by the words 'of a nature or degree' … it will be taken as equivalent to the phrase 'a person of unsound mind' which has been in use hitherto in connection with compulsory detention.* (DHSS, 1960)

As previously mentioned, the section 72(1)(b)(i)[5] of statutory criteria for discharge state that:

> the tribunal shall direct the discharge of a patient liable to be detained ... if they are satisfied –
>
> (i) that he is not then suffering from mental illness, psychopathic disorder, severe mental impairment or mental impairment or from any of those forms of disorder of a nature or degree which makes it appropriate for him to be detained in a hospital for medical treatment;

In this section, we will discuss in turn each of the following key terms: 'degree', 'nature', 'then', 'appropriate' and 'health or safety'.

'Degree'

'Degree' of illness relates to the extent to which mental illness is currently active. Eldergill[6] (1998) suggests that degree is directed towards the current exacerbations and manifestations of disorder. There is no independent or objective measure of degree. The threshold is set by psychiatric opinion and, for any individual, opinion may vary. For members in this study, degree was presumed to exist if the medical member said it existed:

MM ➜ He does have a mental illness of sufficient degree. (RA05)
Pres ➜ Not much doubt that it is a mental illness. It's the degree – is the degree intensive enough?
MM ➜ Yes I'd let it run. (RA08)

Degree was rarely explored further than demonstrated by the RA05 quote above.

'Nature'

The 'nature' of a mental disorder encompasses the characteristics of the patient's condition, its historical course, chronicity and prognosis. In the observed tribunals, there was a tendency to define nature in terms of 'one of the categories of mental disorder outlined in the Act' or in terms of a diagnostic label:

MM ➜ The nature is affective depressive disorder as far as we can tell. (RA01)

Members were presumed to have a shared understanding of diagnostic labels and, therefore, of the nature of the mental disorder under discussion. There were discussions about remission and relapse; but they were held separately from exchanges about the nature of a patient's disorder. The discussions were more commonly linked to compliance (see below for discussion).

'Nature or degree'

A patient must be discharged from section if the tribunal is satisfied that he is not suffering from any of the forms of mental disorder to a 'nature' or 'degree' that makes it appropriate for him to be liable to be detained. Both in the interviews and observed tribunals there was confusion as to whether 'nature or degree' should be read conjunctively or disjunctively. A conjunctive reading requires a tribunal to discharge if the patient is not suffering from a mental disorder *either* of a nature *or* of degree, while a disjunctive reading requires a tribunal to discharge if the mental disorder is not of a nature *and* not of a degree that makes it appropriate for the patient to be liable to be detained.

The distinction between nature and degree is important, not least because it is designed to address two different dimensions of mental disorder. In particular, many mental disorders and mental illnesses are characterised by cycles of remission and relapse. The nature of a patient's mental disorder takes into account that disorder's known characteristics and the patient's previous history of that disorder. Thus, although the degree may not be severe, the nature may be considered serious. Nature may provide a confident prognosis about future degree unless there is therapeutic intervention. There is also a suggestion that the more serious the historical nature of the person's disorder, the less current degree of symptomatology is required and vice versa (MHAC, 1989).

This is demonstrated in a recent case (*R* v. *MHRT South Thames ex parte Smith*). The tribunal found that the applicant's mental disorder was of a nature but not of degree that warranted his detention in a hospital and on that basis did not discharge him. The applicant argued that nature or degree should be read conjunctively; as the tribunal had stated that his disorder was not of a degree warranting his detention he should be discharged from section. In ruling that the tribunal decision was lawful, Justice Popplewell in the Divisional Court accepted that the applicant had a chronic condition that was static, but the condition's nature was such that it might cease to be static. Thus, a patient in remission might not demonstrate the degree of mental disorder sufficient to warrant detention. But, the nature of the patient's disorder, and the patient's medical history, might make liability to detention appropriate. He went on to state that, 'there was a reason for the distinction in the 1983 Act between the words "nature" and "degree" as, if the degree of the disorder alone had to also be considered, it would have been right to direct the discharge even though the nature of the condition was such that it was clear that he should not be discharged'.

The distinction between nature or degree, confirmed by the case above[7], suggests that no degree of current disorder is necessary for continued detention if there is a relevant historical nature. However, bearing in mind that the criteria for discharge do not correspond to the criteria which regulate admission (Eldergill 1998, p. 479), the Mental Health Act Commission's discussion paper (1998) proposes that, regardless of the historical nature of the illness, some degree of symptomatology is required for detention.

In many tribunals, members were challenged by the patient presenting at the hearing without any apparent symptoms of mental disorder:

> *MM* ➔ *In the reasons we have to say that he suffers from mental illness, the evidence of which is? It is pragmatic what you are suggesting but is it lawful? If you follow your argument everyone with schizophrenia could be detained.* (RB05)

Although nature and degree appear to provide some way of more closely defining mental disorder, in practice they introduced confusion.

> *Pres* ➔ *He has been ill but the question is, is he ill now?* (RC15)

> *How do I interpret the 'nature' of a mental illness? Well, I suppose I'm heavily guided by what the medics tell me, both the RMO and our medical member. I mean I wouldn't presume to be able to make a diagnosis myself, so I have to rely on the experts in that area.* (Pres 14)

The absence of external criteria, by which psychiatric diagnoses can be confirmed or refuted (Kendell, 1993, p. 279), left most members reliant upon their subjective opinion or the opinion of the medical experts:

> *Each case is different and each set of facts is going to be different. I suppose if I'm being honest, it's less a question of specific information, and more a question of feel.* (Pres 02)

> *There's no definition of it (*mental illness*) in the Act … it's entirely one's personal judgement.* (MM 03)

With the medical member's guidance, members demonstrated little difficulty in recognising mental disorder. However, determination of the nature or degree of mental disorder was less clear:

> *You've got these three words 'nature', 'degree' and 'then'. And 'then' doesn't actually mean 'then', it means now, but thinking about everything that's happened in the past. 'Degree' does it mean now or does it mean how it used to be and may be again? Well 'nature' isn't clear because does it mean the 'nature' of the condition generally or the 'nature' of the condition of this individual? And you can play with these permutations and make of it what you will.* (MM 10)

'Then'

In the context of nature, the term 'then' seems contradictory because a literal reading would discount the importance of the past and possible future course of the disorder. 'Then' is generally considered to relate to the time of the hearing, as distinct from the time of admission. In a sense, the question posed by the member above – Is he ill now? – was irrelevant. The patient had a mental illness, albeit one controlled by medication. Consequently he was ill, within the definition of the MHA 1983.

'Appropriate'

The term 'appropriate' in the s72(1)(b)(i) criteria for discharge relates to a patient's detention in a hospital for medical treatment. In this study the term was interpreted in a more straightforward way. Eldergill explains 'appropriate' in the following way:

> *Although it is sometimes said that the test set out in section 72(1)(b)(i) is whether it is appropriate to physically detain the patient in hospital, this is something of a simplification. The existence of an authority to detain a patient not only empowers the managers to detain him in the hospital, using restraint if necessary. It also has the necessary consequence that the patient may only leave the ward or hospital with permission and, where necessary, only then with an escort or subject to conditions. The administration of treatment without his consent is also authorised. Accordingly, it might be appropriate for an in-patient to remain 'liable to be detained' even though he would not otherwise immediately leave the hospital. For example because he might otherwise refuse medication; intermittently absent himself in a way that undermines the treatment programme or put himself or others at risk; or intermittently require restraint.* (Eldergill, 1998, p. 487)

Eldergill states that the RMO should 'always be asked to clarify why a power of detention is appropriate'. As possible reasons, he lists the need for restraint, or a period of trial leave, or to prevent the patient discharging himself, refusing necessary treatment, or being intermittently absent (Eldergill, 1998, p. 488). Invariably RMOs were asked for their reasons for the continued detention of their patient and the most common reason that they gave related to fears of non-compliance with treatment, usually medication.

'Health or safety'

Section 72(1)(b)(ii) of the MHA 1983 provides that a tribunal shall discharge a patient if it is satisfied that it is not necessary for the patient's health or safety, or for the protection of others, that he should receive in-patient treatment. According to Eldergill (1998), the issue is whether the considerations – that is, the patient's health or safety, or the need to protect others – necessitate further in-patient treatment, rather than whether the considerations, of themselves, necessitate further detention. As with other aspects of the criteria, members invariably discussed safety, and the need to protect others, as self-contained issues. They were examined in the general context of the risks associated with discharge. Assessing the risk to patients or public might be thought to be more straightforward, being open to interpretation by all tribunal members upon hearing the evidence. However, tribunal members struggled greatly with assessments of risk. We return to this in more detail later.

The standard of proof

A patient must be discharged by a tribunal if the discharge criteria exist. These criteria require the tribunal to be 'satisfied' that the patient is not suffering from mental disorder or from mental disorder of a nature or degree that warrants his detention in hospital... (s. 72(1)(a)(i)). It is not clear, however, what standard of proof the word 'satisfied' imposes. Although there is no case law, it is generally assumed that the standard of proof is the balance of probabilities, with the burden of proof placed on the applicant. Commentators are divided on the degree of certainty to be attached to the notion of being satisfied. Eldergill (1998, p. 569) provides at least seven different interpretations of the word, ranging from being persuaded to satisfied beyond reasonable doubt. In ex parte Ryan[8], Nolan J. stated that satisfied was a fairly strong word.

A tribunal is not obliged to discharge if it is not satisfied that the patient is not suffering from mental disorder or from mental disorder of a nature or degree that warrants detention in hospital. This 'double-negative' effect has been suggested by some authors to increase the discharge threshold, as there can be few circumstances in which a tribunal could be completely satisfied that a mental disorder of the requisite nature or degree did not exist. Depending on how suffering[9] is interpreted, and given that discussion is about mental disorder, the likelihood of a tribunal being satisfied is extremely low and the likelihood of the tribunal being not satisfied extremely high:

> *Pres ➜ We don't need to be satisfied that she is ill. We have to be sure that she is not; and I don't think she is not not ill so she can't be released.* (RA07)

One president suggested that members do not have to be absolutely certain about the presence of mental disorder, as the burden of proof is on the patient and the standard is that of the civil courts, that is on the balance of probabilities (Pres 13). As a result, members may feel that they do not have fully to resolve any uncertainties. Lack of certainty over the presence or absence of mental disorder paralleled the lack of precision over the presence or absence of evidence. This is not helped by the Rules, which allow a tribunal to receive documentary and oral evidence that would be inadmissible in a court of law. This includes hearsay[10] as evidence. Technical rules of evidence form no part of the rules of natural justice, which allow tribunals to use evidence from other hearings, so long as all parties have an opportunity to see and deal with it.

In the tribunals we observed hunch and common-sense, and, adopting a more intuitive approach, replaced the precise application of the legal criteria:

> *I mean I suppose that hard cases make bad law, and if you have a particularly difficult decision, well, fair enough, by not discharging the patient from the section you're erring on the side of caution aren't you? So that's fair enough.* (MM 22)

Each case is different and each set of facts is going to be different. I suppose if I'm being honest, it's less a question of specific information, and more a question of feel. (Pres 02)

MM ➔ *No evidence of paranoid delusional ideas – storming out of room is entirely consistent with a stroppy young man. I am satisfied, however, he has a mental disorder. We don't even need to specify the illness.* (RA15)
Pres ➔ *Do you think he meets the criteria?*
MM ➔ *My intuition is not to discharge because I still feel a hardness of character.* (RD11)

In practice, members addressed the statutory criteria in a circuitous way[11]. They used short-cut techniques similar to the processual approaches identified in Chapter 7. These techniques side-stepped the complexities and nuances of interpretation involved in applying the statutory criteria thoroughly. Members preferred to use certain key concepts as proxies. They included:

- the presence or absence of symptoms;
- the presence or absence of insight;
- compliance and cooperation;
- risk and danger of the patient to other people.

These were also the factors that drove discussion in borderline cases and discussed in Chapter 7.

Symptoms

The manifestation of symptoms by the patient during the tribunal hearing was very important, providing instant legitimisation of the person's mental disorder. Given the lack of clarity about the nature or degree of mental disorder, the absence of symptoms raised the need to consider whether the patient was in fact mentally disordered of a nature or degree which warranted detention. In most cases, there was only a limited attempt to explore the symptoms associated with the nature or degree of mental disorder.

Pres ➔ *Should I say what I think first or what?*
(LM and MM nod in agreement)
Pres ➔ *There is no doubt that he is suffering from mental disorder. He demonstrated it in various ways. He was evasive and showed an unwillingness to face up to reality.*
MM ➔ *Strange mixture – he avoids it at times by saying that the subject doesn't matter any more. At other times he shows deeper delusions.*
Pres ➔ *I am satisfied, whether or not there was a grain of truth, deeper delusions are affecting him. Then we go on to whether treatment requires continued detention. RMO said he wouldn't cooperate and I have no faith in his [*patient's*] statement that he will stay in hospital. RMO said he would have B & B [*reference to absence with leave*] but would head off when the medication was being given out.* (RA04)

The president (above) may have had no doubt that the patient was suffering from mental disorder but the evidence cited for this opinion is not convincing

In the next case, the medical member adopts a different approach to the statutory criteria. There is an attempt to identify the nature and degree of the patient's mental disorder:

> *MM ➜ She has an organic mental state. From conversations this morning she shows organic loss characterised by paranoia. They don't know about it when she is in the community. The death of her niece and sister did contribute to delusional ideas. There has been a deterioration with an increase in memory loss since Christmas. Is there side by side a functional illness? Like depression? Or an underlying illness? Well she didn't express paranoid ideas to me and not today. The nurse said she seemed suspicious on the ward. The evidence is not of the highest quality, the RMO is very junior and has in any case not been here for the whole of her section. We don't know the extent of her delusions nor how she copes at night. Does it matter? Probably not. Her son is very concerned. He feels that her paranoia hasn't faded. The nurse and RMO are very concerned. There is agreement in the notes, but the testing shows that organic comes out borderline. The decision rests on the value placed on paranoia. She doesn't have to be discharged today but there is only one day left of her section. She is settled without medication. I would have no difficulty continuing her detention – indeed arguing for it. The one day is not our problem. Certainly the assessment is incomplete. I think it is a marginal case.* (RA02)

At first glance this report appears more comprehensive. However, the medical member fails to provide any evidence of the symptoms which he says exist. The patient is not on any medication and, according to the medical member, the decision rests on 'the value placed on paranoia'. In another case, evidence of delusions could not be elicited by the medical member either in the tribunal or in his examination of the patient:

> *Pres ➜ There are no new delusions, but they are still there according to the ward.*
> *LM ➜ Yes.*
> *Pres ➜ That is, they're happening now.*
> *MM ➜ That's why I raised it with the nurse.*
> *LM ➜ Yes she suggests that he's still deluded.*
> *Pre ➜ The delusions are there, they are being controlled.*
> *MM ➜ Yes, I think he does still have delusions, to an extent I agree with the RMO he hasn't had enough of a trial yet, but it was difficult to get him to voice a delusion.* (RC01)

In this case the medical member's inability to elicit delusions was not interpreted as the absence of delusions but as the suppression of delusions. It is not clear how a patient in these circumstances could prove that they no longer experienced delusions.

Pres ➜ *He is still suffering but it is controlled …*
Pres ➜ *But there are no overt symptoms at the moment.*
MM ➜ *He is a manic depressive. He has periods of normality and then he blows.*
Pres ➜ *How long do you think he should be subject to a section?*
MM ➜ *He is still mentally ill. He requires to be maintained in hospital for treatment.*
LM ➜ *Is this not a case where the legal framework of supervised discharge would help?*
Pres ➜ *There's one difficulty, supervised discharge relies on cooperation, but is he still ill?*
MM ➜ *If you feel that he is depressed, then discharge doesn't come into it. If you feel he can manage outside there are problems about where to place him.*
Pres ➜ *He is a perfect gentleman.*
MM ➜ *I thought he was only just contained, simmering below the surface.* (RC14)

In the two above examples the absence of symptoms was not interpreted as the absence of mental illness.

Insight

Insight was the single most consistently discussed symptom of mental illness. It was seen as the key to predicting compliance with treatment and thereby the risk were the patient to be discharged. There was divergence between members as to its presence or absence. As with other key concepts, little evidence was produced to support either point of view:

The hearing
LR ➜ *Do you accept that you are ill?*
Pt ➜ *No question about it, I accept it completely.*
LR ➜ *Is it of a nature or degree for you to be in hospital?*
Pt ➜ *No.*
LR ➜ *Are they assessing and treating you here?*
Pt ➜ *Yes.*
LR ➜ *Would you take medication? Your responsible medical officer and social worker say you wouldn't.*
Pt ➜ *I would take it.*
LR ➜ *Why did you tell them you wouldn't?*
Pt ➜ *Because they are keeping me here against my will and it has made me angry.*
LR ➜ *So, would you take it?*
Pt ➜ *Yes, and I would attend the clinic, whatever was required.*
LR ➜ *They also say you have no insight.*
Pt ➜ *Yes I have.*

The deliberation
Pres ➔ *I don't think he has any insight.*
MM ➔ *No, I don't think he would take his medication, he changed his mind, I think I tricked him into answering.*
(The conversation between the legal and the medical member continues without any contribution from the lay member. The lay member suddenly interrupts, in an assertive non-aggressive way.)
LM ➔ *Don't count me in on this. Can I say my thing now? The patient spoke up very well. I am left with the view that hospital is doing him no good. I am persuaded that he has accepted his illness and will cooperate. I am also with the medical member that alcohol is relevant.* (RD15)
The hearing
Pt ➔ *Obviously I know I have a problem and need help.*

The deliberation
LM ➔ *She is without insight.* (RA07)

Statements about insight, without discussion of the relevant evidence, creates a risk of bias. In the above example (RA07) there had been a number of statements from the patient during the hearing which seemed to suggest that the patient recognised a mental health problem for which she was receiving help. In fact, the question of insight had, perhaps unusually, not figured very strongly in this patient's tribunal. However, in the deliberation, the lay member stated that the patient did not have insight and the statement was not challenged by the other tribunal members. There appeared to be no evidence for this statement and it was incorporated into the statement of reasons for continued detention.

Compliance

The need to ensure compliance with medication was frequently seen as crucial, to reduce the risk of relapse, or to ensure the patient's health or safety, or for the protection of others.

MM ➔ *Keeping him in is the only way to treat him.* (RD09)
Pres ➔ *He is ill and of a nature and degree and if not under section will not take medication.* (RA12)
Pres ➔ *It's the nature of the risk – the Mental Health Act states that if well enough on medication patient has to be discharged.* (RD06)

In expressing uncertainty about compliance, it was frequently viewed as an all or nothing state:

MM ➔ *The key thing is medication. She would not take it.* (RC09)

Intermittent compliance was not considered. Evidence for compliance or non-compliance varied. Past non-compliance raised doubts about future compliance. Trust and credibility were major influences on the members' response to patients who said they would take their medication:

MM ➔ *In the past she has stopped taking her medication and relapsed quite quickly.* (RB16)
Pres ➔ *I am uncertain about medication compliance – I do not believe the patient when he says he will comply.* (RD03)

There were rare occasions on which views on compliance were linked to getting other aspects of treatment right. This was important as it restored to the patient a rational basis for non-compliance.

LM ➔ *She needs help with obesity to ensure compliance with medication.* (RD01)
MM ➔ *The main issue is a need to take medication. He is sectioned in order to take the medication. So the real issue is whether he is in or out of episode?*
MM ➔ *In.*
Pres ➔ *That's your decision, you have to guide us.*
MM ➔ *Well I think he is.*
LM ➔ *But he did present well.*
Pres ➔ *Extraordinarily well. He was goaded by his mother, what would happen if he were at home?*
MM ➔ *Probably lots of rowing.*
LM ➔ *If only he'd go somewhere else.*
Pres ➔ *I must say I wouldn't want to live with her. I found her patronising.*
MM ➔ *He wants to be independent, but he's really sick, poor chap. Where he lives is a red herring.*
Pres ➔ *Do you think he is still ill?*
LM ➔ *I am torn between what the nurses say and how he presents. But if we discharge him he will go home and things will get bad very quickly.* (RC15)

In one of the few tribunals in which the patient was discharged, issues of insight and compliance were debated. Unusually, the patient was discharged despite the tribunal's belief that the patient would cease taking medication if discharged. This tribunal (RA13) concerned a 48-year-old man, who had been detained on section 3 for 5.5 months; only 13 days remained of his section. He was diagnosed as having a bipolar affective disorder, and had a long history of contact with the psychiatric services. He was first admitted to hospital 15 years previously, and had had several admissions since then, following relapses in the community ('revolving door' pattern). He had started deteriorating 1–2 months before his current admission to hospital under section. He attributed his deterioration to moving to a new flat, which required a lot of repairs, to the loss of his job/business (although details of this were not followed up in the hearing). He was being treated with a mixture of drugs: lithium, carbamazepine and chlorpromazine. In the pre-hearing meeting the president suggested that they might be recommending a supervised discharge order.

Since being in hospital, evidence was given that his condition had improved, particularly in the last 4–6 weeks, and he had also started taking medication (voluntarily). He was regularly being given leave from hospital, some of which was unescorted. The medical member reported that in the preliminary examination the patient was very calm – not manic, not overly depressed – 'and showed some insight into his illness and treatment'. The RMO's view was that the patient needed longer on section (he was planning to renew the section 3) in order to make a gradual return to the community, and hopefully break the cycle of admissions and relapse. The RMO argued that the patient had been very ill, and that his current mental state was just a 'snapshot' and should be viewed in the overall context of past and future prognosis.

In the deliberation, the medical member of the tribunal argued strongly that on the basis of the patient's presentation at the hearing, the nature and degree of his mental illness were not sufficient for detention. He also felt that his insight might not improve (the main reason given by RMO for continued detention), but believed that he would nonetheless take his medication. Unusually, the tribunal accepted compliance without full insight and the president said – 'He may be back [*to hospital*] but that is not our problem, it is about today'. However, the president also commented that it was 'not an easy one'; and that they had to go on 'the balance of probabilities'. This is an extract from the deliberation.

> *Pres ➜ Insight. Will he ever gain insight? Probably not. Will he ever take his medication voluntarily?*
> *MM ➜ It is difficult to say. Often it's an irrelevance.*
> *Pres ➜ He has 13 days to go on the section. He is very guarded.*
> *MM ➜ I thought he was very open. I don't think he was lying about the medication. He thinks it's stress, he doesn't think he has a mental disorder. But can you keep him on a section? You can't keep him forever.*
> (There ensues some discussion about his treatment.)
> *MM ➜ What do you think?*
> *Pres ➜ Let's take the Act – there's little doubt that he suffers from mental illness – nature or degree? Current symptoms? Controlled by medication.*
> *MM ➜ What he has said is exactly true. There is nothing on the ward, no treatment.*
> *Pres ➜ He is on an open ward, he is not observed, the medication could be given outside.*
> *LM ➜ If there is the will.*
> *Pres ➜ I've little doubt in my mind that he will stop taking medication. Should the section be said to give him the right to treatment? The RMO has come out with a very good report.*
> *MM ➜ But he can't be detained on the basis of that report.* (RA13)
> (patient is discharged)

Risk

Risk was an important and broadly defined concept. It encompassed risk to the patient and to members of the public and included not just 'harm' but also the risk of becoming ill again. Clearly, these two concepts were inter-related; becoming ill again might bring a risk of harm. For this reason, members were concerned to understand the nature of the patient's disorder in terms of propensity to relapse.

MM ➔ *It is a longstanding relapsing illness.* (RD01)
MM ➔ *It is of nature since it will relapse unless he gets treatment.* (RD06)
MM ➔ *The real concern is the risk of relapse – I am not concerned with the risk to others.* (RA01)

For patients with a long history of mental illness it was possible to map the frequency and nature of relapses.

Members recognised that past behaviour is a good predictor of future behaviour and used this principle to predict the likelihood of violence:

MM ➔ *Best predictor of violence is what has happened in the past.* (RD12)

However, the maxim did not serve members well in an environment in which there is often not much certainty, little proper record, and a lack of clarity about past behaviour, particularly alleged violent events. Members were not well equipped to establish the accuracy of recorded past behaviour and, in particular, to assess the context within which past behaviour had occurred. The circumstances within which violence has in the past occurred is recognised to be an important component of prediction (Coid, 1996). Of course for newly diagnosed patients or those with little previous contact with mental health services there was little previously recorded history on which to base predictions.

In only a few tribunal deliberations did medical members use research evidence to support their views on risk.

MM ➔ *15 per cent of manic depressive illnessess result in the person killing themselves.* (RD10)

In the absence of good data about predictors of violence and good information on past behaviour, other indicators were substituted as predictors. In particular, the demeanour and personality of the patient become important. It was extremely common for members to express concerns about the risk of violence on the basis of little or no evidence.

MM ➔ *I am very worried about him being discharged. Notwithstanding the fact that he presented so well today we would be unwise to discharge him.* (RA15)
LM ➔ *Keep on section because he needs care, planned care – otherwise he will deteriorate. We need to prevent harm.* (RC04)
MM ➔ *I think he's dangerous. I can see why people are afraid of him.* (RC02)
Pres ➔ *He's certainly dangerous.* (RB01)
LM ➔ *I hate to think about him wandering around the community.* (RC11)
MM ➔ *I'm sure he's not harmful but very intimidating.* (RC09)

On a few occasions the tribunal president sounded a cautionary note about the basis for comments about risk and violence.

Pres ➔ *Second-hand evidence of actual violence is dangerous.* (RA10)

Tribunal members also constructed worst-case scenarios in which they speculated as to the worst outcome were the patient to be discharged.

LM ➔ *If lifted what is the worst that can happen – he'd be brought back into hospital.* (RD15)
MM ➔ *The point is who is damaged by it; he's not going to kill himself.* (RD09)
MM ➔ *The worst risk is that he would end up in the criminal justice system.* (RB06)
Pres ➔ *Everyone agrees that the chap has threatened her. Back to what is degree of risk – relapse is one thing – aggressive behaviour another. Everyone says she is a low risk.* (RB07)

In the interviews there was a recognition that the MHA 1983 gave tribunal members the freedom to take risky decisions. In the observed tribunals, however, the risks of 'getting it wrong' seemed so great that members appeared to gather evidence to justify not discharging rather than actively pursuing the possibility of discharge. Even though tribunal members recognised that most patients with mental illness do not pose a danger to themselves or the community, this was one of the most important elements of their discussions.

But I think that people are easily frightened into taking no risk decisions. And I think that it's inherent to our position that we must be free to take some risk. We should not be in a position that we're terrified to take any risk at all. We must be able to discharge patients knowing that there is some risk. And indeed the Act actually quantifies it, by giving us a discretion, even if the patient is mad, even if the patient is dangerous, we still have a discretion to discharge. That I think makes very clear that we must be in a position to exercise a risk jurisdiction. And I think we do nobody any favours if we just lock everybody up and say no, no, we're taking no risks at all. And that's why I think we need feedback. If we know what percentage of our discharge decision went wrong, we would be much reassured by that. (Pres 02)

As part of testing the idea about whether a patient could manage and be managed in the community there were a number of circumstances in which the RMO had granted a patient leave under section 17 of the MHA 1983[12]. Absence with leave enables the RMO to test the progress that has been made; and periods of trial leave were seen both as minimising risks and providing evidence of an improved or stable mental state. In this respect section 17 leave signalled to tribunal members that the patient was not felt by the RMO to be a great risk and provided evidence of how patients were able to manage in the community. However, there was no clarity about the period of leave required to provide this reassurance.

MM ➔ *He has recovered well from this recent episode... He is likely to relapse very quickly if he stops medication. I'm not sure about keeping him on section with so much section 17 leave. We were always told a week or two – it was only for a matter of weeks you could legally do it.*

Pres ➜ *It probably will be that by the time it comes to renew the section.*
MM ➜ *I have a feeling things have shifted. It is now acceptable practice to keep this amount of leave on until the end of the section.*
Pres ➜ *Does this amount of leave warrant being sectioned? But if he is not on section, there is no compulsion to take medication.*
MM ➜ *They are giving medication to suppress it. I agree from the medical point of view that it is safer to impose medication until the period at which the section ends.*
Pres ➜ *I wouldn't let someone out of hospital unless I regarded the condition as incurable.* (RC07)

In another case (RB05) where the patient was having significant amounts of leave, the medical member asserted that the patient could not be legally detained on the grounds that the patient was no longer suffering from a mental illness. The medical member also stated that it was not lawful to continue detention under the Mental Health Act just to ensure that the patient continued to take his medication. The president and lay member considered that the patient should remain on section while awaiting a place in a hostel. The provision of this place was considered to offer the patient the best hope of maintaining improvement and stability within a supportive setting.

Two further topics were discussed in relation to risk: the social circumstances of the patient; and views on the treatment the patient had received in hospital.

Social circumstances

In the tribunals we observed members were particularly poorly served with information about the social circumstances of patients. Reports were frequently prepared by someone other than the patient's key worker (where they had had one), and the information rarely gave sufficient detail on family and support networks or the nature of patients' abilities to look after themselves:

LM ➜ *I am amazed that no one knows about community support.* (RA02)
Pres ➜ *Are we keeping her in hospital because of her background circumstances? Only a third hand account of voices and assault.* (RA09)

In many section 3 tribunals the social circumstances report had been prepared some time before the hearing and social workers were unable to provide up-to-date information.

LM ➜ *Can you update this report? It is quite old now.*
SW[13] ➜ *I haven't seen Danielle*[14] *since the birth of her child. I last saw her three months ago, so I can't comment on any assessment of her since then.* (RD13)
Pres ➜ *Is there anything you want to add to the report?*
SW ➜ *No I haven't seen her or spoken to her since the report was written.*
LM ➜ *What is your involvement with her?*
SW ➜ *I visit her at home or she comes to the office about once a month.* (RD10)

Community psychiatric nurses (CPN) were viewed by social workers as being likely to have more regular contact with the patient once in the community than they had. In the tribunals the social workers described their input as confined to the period around admission and discharge and if any social difficulties arose once at home CPNs would alert the social worker to these difficulties.

> *LM* ➜ *What would your involvement be if patient was discharged home?*
> *SW* ➜ *I wouldn't be involved much it would be the CPN. She would do fortnightly visits. I would only be called in if there were difficulties.* (RD06)

Not surprisingly, given the nature and purpose of tribunals, there were rarely any comprehensive plans for the patient's after-care in the community.

> *MM* ➜ *We can't return him to anything even if we got him better.* (RC02)

This absence of social support, in the minds of the tribunal members, greatly increased the risks of relapse were this patient to be discharged.

Views of treatment received in hospital

Member's views of the patient's treatment should have been important in relation to whether that treatment needed to be provided in hospital and indeed whether the patient was treatable. However, there were a number of occasions on which concerns were expressed at the inadequacy of the treatment being received while in hospital:

> *LM* ➜ *What is the point of taking away someone's liberty if they don't address the factors that brought her in?* (RD13)
> *LM* ➜ *He is not well served by being where he is.* (RC12)
> *MM* ➜ *Hopefully we are doing him a favour [*by continuing his detention*], he needs that time so hospital can sort themselves out. We want to say something optimistic.* (RC10)

However, members were very conscious in the interviews of the dangers of using the tribunal solely for therapeutic purposes:

> *As much as I would like to help somebody in a lot of cases, that is not my function – my function is quite specific, it's within the confines of an Act.* (Pres 01)

> *The danger that has to be guarded against I think is that you slip into simply doing what you think is best for somebody or doing what's in their interests and that's a medical paradigm which I don't think applies in legal circles.* (Pres 07)

A number of presidents in the interviews expressed a desire to have the power to influence the provision of resources in the community, and to enforce any recommendations they might make:

> *I suppose I regret that the tribunal doesn't have wider powers, and that it can't actually look at the question of where would this person better be?* (Pres 02)
> *I think there is some frustration ... that we can't make serious recommendations about the future treatment of the patient, or their future care ... and if we do nobody takes any notice.* (Pres 19)

Outcome data

Members demonstrated that they had problems making decisions in the context of little outcome information. They had little understanding of what degree of mental illness could be contained in the community or the relative importance of insight in determining compliance with medication. There were, however, mixed views on receiving follow-up information for those patients who had been discharged by a tribunal:

> *If we knew what percentage of our discharge decisions went wrong, we would be much reassured by that.* (Pres 02)
> *I think it's better not to know. The job is about making a decision on the day and then leaving it behind.* (MM03)
> *You don't stop the door revolving by lengthening a discharge now or by not discharging.* (Pres 02)

Summary

The tribunal members in this study experienced many difficulties understanding, interpreting and applying the statutory criteria for discharge. The study has shown that although members were familiar with the language of the MHA 1983, they did not always know how to apply them to the evidence they had heard.

As this chapter has shown, tribunal members in the observed tribunals recognised that mental illness may be present even when symptoms are absent through medication control and that the absence of symptoms is not indicative of the absence of mental illness. Further, members operated from a framework in which the nature or degree of mental illness that makes a patient liable to be detained in hospital takes in not just the patient's present mental state but the history of the condition.

A precise understanding of the nature and degree of mental illness was supplanted by other concepts. Insight, compliance with treatment and particularly medication and risk were seen as central determinants of whether the statutory criteria were fulfilled. The reliance on clinical assessment and on judgements and opinion often elicited conflicting and confusing evidence. However, tribunal members did not appear to feel that they had to be absolutely certain about the accuracy of the evidence presented in the tribunal and this greatly facilitated decision-making.

Notes

1 The statutory criteria for discharge from section 3 will be taken as the starting point. Where particular reference is made to section 2 cases this will be made explicit.
2 Review of the Mental Health Act 1959, Cmnd. 7320 (1978).
3 *W* v. *L* [1974] Q.B. 711; [1973] 3 W.L.R. 859, CA.
4 *R* v. *Trent MHRT, ex parte Hayes*, 9 May 1985, CA.
5 These criteria relate to admission to hospital for medical treatment under section 3 of the MHA (1983).
6 I draw heavily on the interpretations suggested by Eldergill (1998).
7 *R* v. *MHRT for S. Thames Region, ex parte Smith* (1998).
8 *R* v. *Trent MHRT, ex parte Ryan* [1992] C.O.D. 157, D.C.
9 So long as it is necessary for a person to be under treatment for a disease or disability, then that person must be held to be suffering from that disease or disability based on the *Devon County Council* v. *Hawkins* [1967] Q.B. 26.
10 Tribunals are entitled to act on any material that is logically probative even though it would not be admissible as evidence in a court of law. Evidence is relevant if it is logically probative or disprobative of some matter that requires proof and all evidence is *prima facie* admissible (Eldergill, 1998, p. 811).
11 Not forgetting that in 11 cases there was no discussion at all.
12 At any time section 17 leave can be revoked by the RMO serving the patient written notice. The RMO may do so as long as the patient's condition makes the patient liable to detention in hospital for treatment. A tribunal is not obliged, by virtue of section 72(1)(b)(i), to discharge a patient who has leave to reside at home or in a hostel unless it is also satisfied that it is inappropriate for him to remain liable to be detained in a hospital for further medical treatment.
13 SW = social worker.
14 Not patient's real name.

9

The Decision

Tribunals must give a written statement of the reasons for their decisions (SI 1983 No. 942, Part V, Rule 23). In this chapter we examine the process by which decisions were recorded on the decision forms (see Appendix 5) and the content of the decisions.

Patients were discharged in five of the observed tribunals (see Table 9.1). All but one discharge concerned a patient detained under section 2. One discharge was deferred to allow appropriate arrangements to be made, in the community, for the patient's return home. In addition, three tribunals recommended that the patient be transferred to another hospital. In another case, the hearing was adjourned (RD01) and scheduled to reconvene one month later. The tribunal did not reconvene because the RMO discharged the patient in the intervening period.

The guidance

None of the presidents participating in the interview stage of this study had received any formal training in writing the decision. Over time, however, communications in tribunal newsletters and advice from the regional chairmen had provided some specific guidance. The Notes, previously mentioned, formed the most comprehensive guidance on the writing of the decision. The *Guide for Members* states that the reasons for the decision need not be elaborate but they 'must deal with the substantial points which have been raised and must show the parties the basis on which the tribunal has acted'. It goes on to say that, although 'it is not usually necessary to review the evidence at length', it is 'important to say which evidence has been accepted or rejected' (1996b, p. 11).

The Notes[1] (*hereafter referred to as the 'Notes'*) for guidance when completing the reasons section of the decision forms state that:

1. The 'STATEMENT OF REASONS' for the Tribunal's decision and recommendations must be understood by the patient, his advisers and those caring for him. Moreover, in the event of a judicial review, or any other form of appeal, this part of the form will receive detailed scrutiny.

Table 9.1 *Tribunal outcomes*

Outcome of tribunal	Region 1	Region 2	Region 3	Region 4	Total
Continued detention	14*	15**	13	14	56
Discharge from section	1	1	2	1	5

Notes: * includes 1 recommendation for transfer to another hospital
** includes 2 recommendations for transfer to another hospital

2. A Mental Health Review Tribunal must never be regarded as a contest between the patient and the detaining authority, but in every case it is important to demonstrate to all the parties involved that their written and verbal evidence has been fairly considered.
3. It is vital therefore, that the reasons are clearly stated, that it is readily apparent that they are based on evidence provided and that sound judicial principles have been logically applied.
4. When completing the 'STATEMENT OF REASONS' sections of the Decision Forms there are three main principles to be borne in mind:
   a) A mere repetition of the statutory criteria is both wrong and unnecessary as these are already detailed elsewhere on the form.
   b) The reasons should explain why main arguments or matters of evidence have been accepted or rejected.
   c) They should contain an explanation as to why the decision follows the facts found.
5. It is suggested that these requirements can usually be met by adopting the procedures set out below:
   a) Summarise briefly the facts and arguments advanced by or on behalf of the Applicant and other main witnesses.
   b) State which facts and arguments were accepted and which were rejected, saying why.

The president has specific responsibility for recording the tribunal decision, and in this study was always responsible for the initial drafting of the decision. Once the decision had been drafted and agreed it was either dictated to the tribunal clerk to be written on the Statement of Reasons for Decision Form or on rare occasions the decision was actually written on the form by the tribunal president. As emphasised in the Notes (above), the Statement of Reasons is particularly important, in terms of public accountability and as evidence in any judicial review of the decision[2].

Structure and content of the 'Statement of Reasons'

There was great consistency across all tribunals in terms of the structure, content and style of the written Statement of Reasons with only a small minority of the statements not addressing the elements described in the Notes. The majority of all Statements of Reasons contained the following core elements:

- The patient is currently suffering from .... (*description of diagnosis*)
- This is characterised by .... (*description of signs and symptoms*)
- The evidence for this is .... (*whose accounts were believed*)
- The patient's condition requires .... (*treatment*)
- The patient's response to treatment
- The patient needs to be detained in the interests of .... (*own health and safety*)
- If discharged ....
- Outcome: discharged/not discharged.

In the interviews, tribunal presidents acknowledged the importance of the Statement of Reasons as the formal record of the outcome of the hearing. However, while the content of the Statement of Reasons reflected elements of the hearing, it was less easy to describe the relationship between the deliberation and the Statement of Reasons. Very good and comprehensive Statement of Reasons could and did arise in the absence of any discussion in the deliberation.

The following comprehensive Statement of Reasons resulted from a five-minute deliberation.

> *The application is dismissed. The patient is an intelligent man who is able to express himself very well. He has in the past run a successful business. It is only since 1993 that he has had five admissions to hospital for psychiatric treatment. He has very little insight into his present condition which he attributes to stress. He does not think that he needs medication and the tribunal fears that if he were to be discharged he would very soon cease to take it, which according to the evidence would within 6–8 weeks result in his readmission. We are predominantly concerned for the patient's own welfare but it has to be said that there is an element of risk to other people. He himself described damaging property and taking his girlfriend by the throat last Christmas when he was annoyed by her actions.*
>
> *He is now benefiting from a considerable amount of leave and understandably describes his stay in hospital as bed and breakfast. He has made considerable progress and there is a plan to progress him out of the hospital but in the meantime he needs the control of the section to ensure that he takes his medication.* (RC07)

In two tribunals where there was barely any (see RB09, page 80) or no discussion at all in the deliberation, the Statement of Reasons were concise.

> *The tribunal accepts the RMO's evidence in its entirety. The patient very clearly continues to suffer from mental illness and requires restraint. He requires to be detained under section for his own health and safety and for the protection of others. He is presently appropriately detained.* (RB09)

> *The patient has a longstanding mental illness which is responding reasonably well to drugs. He has had several periods in hospital but unfortunately when*

he has been re-established in the community he has broken down, partly because of his recreational use of drugs.

We are satisfied that the order is necessary and indeed advantageous to his progress. Plans are being developed for future advances and we feel it would be wrong at this stage to remove the safeguard of the order and possibly interrupt his progress. (RC03)

In all cases where the tribunal opted to discharge the patient from section, the Statement of Reasons contained a full and detailed explanation of the decision.

We fully understand the dilemma facing the Responsible Medical Officer and the social workers involved with deciding whether or not to detain the patient under Section 2 of the Mental Health Act. The patient has, on her admission, been obliged to take the anti-psychotic drug Stelazine for a 6 month period in 1995 because of her taking a drink spiked with LSD. Again, the situation since her return to live with her mother had become increasingly tense. Furthermore the patient could well find it very difficult to find suitable accommodation if she is not able to return to her mother's and to her boyfriend who also has health and employment problems. However, having listened to the evidence of the RMO who is unable to say whether the patient is suffering from mental illness or not (a view shared by her ASW) and having heard the evidence of the Staff Nurse who stated that the patient had been rational since admission, we do not consider that the patient is suffering from a mental disorder meriting her detention and she should be discharged from detention. Having said that, we do urge the patient to confirm that accommodation is available before leaving the clinic and in any event to listen carefully to the advice of the RMO who has her best interests at heart. (RC05)

Although the reasons accompanying a decision to discharge a patient were usually detailed, there appeared to be no consistent relationship between the length of time spent discussing the evidence after the hearing and the length and detail of the Statement of Reasons.

In her study of mental health review tribunals, Peay remarked:

given that the process of decision-making cannot be open to inspection, it is vital that comprehensive reasons be required. In turn, this would make it less easy for tribunals to neglect the statutory criteria and place more emphasis on the need to justify decisions through reference to the evidence presented, thereby ensuring that presentation of the reasons does not merely conceal a choice, whether conscious or not, to fit the facts to the law. [Peay, 1989, p. 219]

The findings of this study suggest that although tribunals have become better at recording reasons for their decision since Peay carried out her study, the process by which a decision is reached remains variable.

The process

The Tribunal and Inquiries Act states that 'Any statement of the reasons for a decision forms part of the decision'[3]. Consequently, it might be expected that a tribunal's Statement of Reasons would reflect the private deliberations leading to the decision.

In theory the process of writing the Statement of Reasons should be a distinct phase of the deliberation. Logically, it could be assumed that the deliberation would start with discussions about the evidence. A decision would be reached and the Statement of Reasons would draw on the elements of the discussion relevant to the decision. While it could be argued that the first two phases should involve all members of the tribunal, the actual writing of the Statement of Reasons can only physically be done by one person. The drafting of the Statement of Reasons is recognised as the responsibility of the president of the tribunal who must sign the Statement of Reasons form. The clerks, at the time of this study were responsible for ensuring that the decision is communicated to all parties within the time limits laid down in the Rules.

In all of the observed tribunals the president of the tribunal was in charge of writing the Statement of Reasons.

> *To ensure that the decision is one which complies with the law, and which is correctly as it were, accounted for. So I always write the decision, although I always read it to the other members and ensure that they agree with the terms of it.* (Pres 02)

However, as has been discussed in Chapter 8, the way in which decisions were reached varied enormously. There were instances in which the Statement of Reasons was written by the president without any prior discussion with the other tribunal members. In two of the tribunals in which there was no discussion at all, the president began to draft the Statement of Reasons as soon as the hearing had ended and the patient had left the room. The medical and lay tribunal members sat in silence as the president drafted the reasons in his notebook. When it had been drafted, the president read aloud the text he had written. Having finished reading the Statement of Reasons, in both cases the president looked at the other members as if seeking a response. Members indicated they were happy with the wording of the reasons and the presidents then began dictating the Statement of Reasons to the clerks.

In a further nine tribunal deliberations there was a very limited exchange of views (see page 97). Following these minimal interactions, the president began writing the Statement of Reasons and only occasionally consulted other members on the use of a word or when seeking confirmation about something reported during the tribunal.

> *Pres* ➔ *My intuition is not to discharge – we need to justify ourselves.* (RD11)

However, in two cases the president actively involved the medical member in the process. Once discussion had taken place and a decision had been reached, the president explicitly asked the medical member whether there were any particular aspects of the patient's illness and/or treatment that he wished to bring out. In addition, there were a small number of other tribunals in which the president read out the reasons as he was writing. This enabled other tribunal members, usually the medical member, to contribute to the wording of the decision in a more informal way.

The extent to which the medical and lay members participated in the drafting of the decision varied. Medical members consistently contributed more than lay members to the actual drafting of the decision, and not surprisingly, their contribution centred on the diagnosis and treatment of the patient.

In all cases, the Statement of Reasons were written to support the outcome – usually a decision not to discharge. As a result the decision did not usually explain why main arguments or matters of evidence were rejected.

Influences on the Statement of Reasons

Tribunal members both in the interviews and observations recognised that there was a balance to be struck between justifying a decision and providing a full and detailed account of the reasons for a decision. One relatively newly appointed president described how in tribunal member meetings, both regional and national, there had been an emphasis on restricting the length of the Statement of Reasons.

> *If you wrote out the reasons in a format which were longer than a paragraph you were wasting everybody's time. And I was quite angry about all that really.* (Pres 07)

It was also felt by members that detailed reasons in support of a decision not to discharge might adversely affect the progress a patient had made or might open up the possibility of a challenge from the patient. The proceedings of a tribunal may be challenged either by applying to the High Court for Judicial Review under Order 53 of the Rules of the Supreme Court or by requiring the tribunal to state a case for the determination by the High Court on a point of law under s. 78(8). Neither gives a right of appeal against the merits of the decision as such (Hoggett, 1996).

Three cases, in which a tribunal's decision had been challenged[4], had highlighted the widely acknowledged need for tribunal decisions to provide all parties with adequate information to demonstrate that the tribunal had not made an error in law in reaching its finding of fact.

In the interviews, presidents highlighted the difficulties associated with writing the Statement of Reasons. None of the presidents participating in this study had had training in this aspect of their tribunal role before they had had to undertake it. Not surprisingly, several presidents reported in the interviews that writing the decision had provoked considerable anxiety when they had first started to preside at tribunals:

> *When I first started … I found it incredibly difficult to just sit down immediately after a tribunal and write the reasons because you don't have a great deal of time to think about it.* (Pres 20)

Writing the decision was a skilled task, particularly given the pressure of time, and the need to synthesise complex information elicited during a lengthy hearing. While learning the business of crafting a decision may have been difficult, all of the presidents observed in this study skilfully and with apparent ease drafted a Statement of Reasons. It was as though presidents had adopted or internalised a formulaic approach to decision writing.

There was widespread recognition both in the interviews and the observed tribunals that the Statement of Reasons not only had to stand the test of judicial scrutiny, but also had to be sensitive to the audience:

> *It's the whole issue about sensitivity in dealing with the patient himself … your decision-making and your written decision I would guess would have to reflect that sensitivity because they've got to see the decision at the end of the day and to understand how the roles of different people work.* (Pres 01)

While in the hearing it was important to safeguard the relationship between the RMO and the patient, it was equally important, in writing the Statement of Reasons, to protect relationships between the patient and others, which would continue after the tribunal. This frequently resulted in the tribunal members agreeing to omit information that might upset the family or applicant.

> *MM* ➜ *We don't need to hammer him. He is a bright boy, the relationship with the doctor has got to remain long after we have gone.* (RD02)
> *Pres (*starts to write the reasons, but stops and reads out*)* ➜ *In the interests of the safety of others. I think we should leave it out, although it's in the back of everyone's mind.* (RD11)

In addition, there were cases in which, unknown to the patient, friends or relatives had provided critical evidence concerning the patient's mental health or circumstances. Although such evidence might have formed an important part of the deliberation, it was not necessarily reflected in the 'Statement of Reasons'. Members also showed a strong desire to say something positive about the patient's progress:

> *Pres* ➜ *We want to say something optimistic.* (RC10)
> *Pres* ➜ *We need to frame conclusions that are helpful to him and deal with the evidence we've heard.* (RC11)

Occasionally, members used the Statement of Reasons to signal to the RMO concerns about the patient's treatment. In one instance (RC12) tribunal members felt that an RMO had demonstrated contempt for the tribunal, disregarded and dismissed the patient's previous treatment and used the issue of resources as justification for the lack of plans for the patient's future management. In their Statement of Reasons they wrote:

> *The section should continue but we hope that the difficulties in identifying and funding a forensic psychologist will be rapidly resolved so that progress may be made towards rehabilitation.* (RC12)

Given the length of hearings and the complexity of the evidence heard, the Statement of Reasons is necessarily selective. This study suggests that there are a number of influences on what is included and what is left out of the Statement of Reasons. Richardson, in her report to the ESRC on a study of the impact of judicial review on the mental health review tribunal (Award No. R000237006), reported that the reasons cannot 'be relied upon to provide an accurate and full account of the issues covered at the hearing' (Richardson, 1999, p. 28). In particular, she reports a lack of match between the emphasis in the hearing on risk and that reported in the reasons. Although in approximately three-quarters of the observed tribunals 'risk' was a central theme running through the hearings, this was only reflected in about a third of the Statement of Reasons. In this study the greatest mismatch was between the Statement of Reasons and what preceded it in the deliberation.

Summary

The Statement of Reasons provided by the tribunal is extremely important because it communicates the official outcome of the tribunal to the patient. The Notes suggest that it is important to demonstrate that the written and verbal evidence has been fairly considered and that when completing the Statement of Reasons there should be an explanation of why main arguments or matters of evidence have been accepted or rejected.

This study suggests that there a number of influences on what gets recorded in the Statement of Reasons. Factors include the nature of the discussion in the deliberation, the need to protect the doctor–patient relationship and the relationship of the patient to other family members, and a desire to minimise the impact on the patient of a decision not to discharge. However, while the Statement of Reasons may conform to the requirements laid out in the Notes, they cannot be relied on to demonstrate that the evidence in the tribunal has been considered fairly or indeed at all by all three tribunal members, since comprehensive Statement of Reasons were drafted in the complete absence of any discussion in the deliberation.

Notes

1 These were the notes which were being used at the time of the study: ref MG/MH319/1.
2 Judicial review of decisions does not provide patients with an appeal against the finding of facts. The court intervenes in those circumstances in which the tribunal's decision is deemed unlawful, irrational, or improper. Eldergill (1998, p. 857) points out that 'almost every successful application concerning the statute has involved a tribunal exceeding its jurisdiction (exercising a power which it did not have) or failing to give adequate and proper reasons for its decision.
3 Tribunal and Inquiries Act 1992 s. 10(6).
4 *Bone* v. *Mental Health Review Tribunal* [1985] 3 All E.R. 330/*R.* v. *Mental Health Review Tribunal, ex p. Clatworthy* [1985] 3 All E.R. 699/*R.* v. *Mental Health Review Tribunal, ex p. Pickering* [1986] 1 All E.R. 99. Eldergill (1998) explores these and other cases in detail.

10

Discussion

Mental health review tribunals (MHRTs) were established under the Mental Health Act (MHA) 1959 as one of the 'main safeguards against improper admission under compulsory powers' and 'unduly protracted detention'[1]. The 1959 MHA was designed to be enabling rather than regulatory, permitting the maximum of discretion within a loose framework. The statutory provisions were tightened in the 1983 MHA in an attempt to provide a better safeguard for the rights of patients (MHA Commission 1985). Whether the changes fundamentally affected the way in which tribunals dealt with cases is debatable.

It is clear, however, that tribunals are based on compromise. The process of the courts is elaborate, slow and costly, in order, it is argued, to deliver the highest standard of justice. Tribunals provide quicker more accessible justice and undoubtedly some of their problems arise from the need to balance the quality of process against convenience.

This study set out to examine how MHRTs make decisions about whether or not to discharge patients detained under sections 2 and 3 of the Mental Health Act (1983). As has been shown, the research identified significant differences in operation between tribunals from the pre-hearing meeting through to the deliberation. Such was the degree of variation that questions must be raised about the extent to which tribunals in general can be said to provide a safeguard against unduly protracted detention in hospital. Four factors were found to constrain the fairness of tribunal decision-making. These were:

(i) tribunal structure and procedure;
(ii) the legislation, and in particular the section 72 criteria for discharge;
(iii) the actual process of decision-making;
(iv) training.

(i) Tribunal structure and procedure

MHRTs should be conducted in accordance with the basic principles of natural justice; notably the patient has a right to be heard and the proceedings should be fair. In all of the observed tribunals, patients were provided with the opportunity to present their case. Without exception they were dealt with in a sympathetic and caring manner. It is in relation to fairness that tribunals may be criticised. There are a number of aspects of the tribunal procedure which, when taken together, raise concerns about fairness.

By the time the hearing starts, members will have read the case for detaining the patient as presented by the responsible medical officer (RMO) in his report. In a number of the observed tribunals the case for detention was further endorsed by the medical member of the tribunal, in the pre-hearing meeting report on their examination of the patient. The patient is not required to submit a similar statement in support of their case for release from detention. It is difficult to assess the impact on tribunal members of reading only the case for detention in advance of the hearing, but in this study it appeared to provide an early signal of the importance of the medical view over the patient's view.

The role of the medical member both as a fact-finder and a decision-maker is highly problematic. The legal and lay members rely on the clinical judgement of the medical member for interpretation of the statutory criteria. How, and when, this independent view is disclosed is extremely important. As we have highlighted, the medical member frequently disregarded what the *Guide for Members* (1996b) suggests is good practice, by giving a direct opinion on the patient's suitability for discharge. In some cases, this extended to instructing other members on how to interpret the replies that the patient would give in the hearing. In the interviews, medical members demonstrated knowledge of the 'correct procedure' but sometimes chose to disregard it.

Furthermore, the medical member's view plays a role in the deliberative process but is not considered part of the evidence and is thus not open to cross-examination by the patient. It is not possible to quantify the impact of the medical member's views on the final decision but, given the weight attributed to clinical evidence, it is likely to be significant.

From the very beginning of the tribunal process, members will be drawing conclusions about the patient, on the basis of the case for detention. Once members have processed this information, they will find it almost impossible to erase or reinterpret. This phenomenon has been demonstrated repeatedly in studies which examine jurors' exposure to evidence or information that they are asked subsequently to discount when reaching a decision:

- Studies where subjects are instructed to erase or unlearn information show that subjects cannot erase previously learned information (Bjork, 1972);
- Studies that attempt to get decision-makers to divert their attention away from inferior evidence which may subsequently bias judgement show that it rarely works (Casper and Benedict, 1993); and finally
- Studies that examine a subject's ability to reconsider a judgement when instructed that the evidence on which it was based is invalid, show that a subject's inability to rejudge a situation or reverse the influence of the invalid information is so extreme, that the phenomenon has been labelled the 'perseverance effect' (Ross *et al.*, 1975).

The presentation of medical evidence by the tribunal medical member was recognised as a problem by the Council on Tribunals (The Annual Report of the Council on Tribunals, 1983). Their solution was that tribunal members should be instructed to attach no weight to such statements. However, in the light of the previously cited studies, this does not seem likely to be an effective strategy and the evidence from this study indicates that it was not.

Regions adopted different policies as to whether the evidence of the patient was taken first or last. Equally valid reasons were offered for both policies. However, where the patient's evidence was taken last and the RMO's first it was usual for the president to allow the RMO to leave the tribunal once their evidence had been given. This created difficulties where the patient offered a different interpretation of events from the RMO as it prevented the tribunal from returning to question the RMO and perhaps resolve the difference or discrepancy in the evidence.

(ii) The legislation

One of the major challenges to fairness arose from the complex wording of the legislation with which tribunals struggled. As a consequence tribunal members varied in their use and interpretation of the statutory criteria for discharge.

The statutory criteria for discharge draw on two paradigms – legal and medical. The legal paradigm seeks to impose controls on clinical judgement so that noone can be detained indefinitely on the basis of a diagnosis. The medical paradigm seeks to provide treatment, if necessary without consent, for people deemed to be suffering from a mental illness or disorder.

In assessing whether continued compulsory detention is necessary, tribunals have to address the question of whether the patient's mental illness/disorder is of a nature or degree that makes it appropriate for continued detention in hospital. The tribunal must discharge the patient if they are satisfied that the patient is not suffering from mental illness, psychopathic disorder, severe mental impairment or mental impairment or from any of those forms of disorder of a nature or degree which makes it appropriate for him/her to be detained in a hospital for medical treatment. In arriving at a decision about the patient's mental health, tribunal members are dependent on two main sources of clinical expertise: that of the tribunal medical member and that of the RMO. How the patient presents at the tribunal and what the patient says contributes to the body of clinical evidence, but rarely was the patient considered to hold an 'expert' opinion on their own condition.

The patient's mental state, the uncertainties of psychiatric diagnosis and treatment, and the implications of that mental state for discharge, are not matters of fact but of judgement. Although clinical evidence is crucial to the decision-making process, it has to be considered within the legal framework. The difficulties faced by tribunal members interpreting the clinical evidence according to the statutory criteria for discharge have been discussed in Chapter 8. Both in the observations and in the interviews tribunal members grappled with a range of possible interpretations of the section 72 criteria for discharge. Four factors were consistently used as proxies for the section 72 criteria. These were the presence or absence of (i) symptoms, (ii) insight, (iii) compliance and cooperation, and (iv) risk and danger to the patient and other people.

The criteria and the accompanying Rules provide MHRTs with considerable discretion in the way they reach a decision. This discretion is both a strength and a weakness. On the one hand, discretion enables the tribunal to adopt a sensitive and informal manner when reviewing vulnerable patients. On the other hand, discretion dilutes the legislative basis for decision-making by allowing a strict interpretation of the law to be suspended in certain instances. Discretion promotes consideration of each case on its own merits, such that ostensibly similar cases may be treated in different ways. Faced with complex statutory criteria, this study suggests that tribunal members used their discretion to interpret the law in a more accessible way by substituting more tangible criteria based on the factors highlighted above.

However, the precise detail of the statutory criteria is important. The distinction between nature and degree is designed to address two different dimensions of mental disorder. As previously discussed, the 'nature' of a patient's mental disorder takes into account that disorder's known characteristics and the patient's previous history of that disorder, while 'degree' of illness relates to the extent to which mental illness is currently active. This cannot be assessed solely by reference to the presence or absence of symptoms, insight or compliance or perceptions about potential risk.

(iii) Decision-making

There were few procedural rules in operation at the time of this research to guide decision-making in the deliberation, but it could be assumed that the value of having three tribunal members rests in their contribution to decision-making. The Leggatt Review (2001) stated that choosing a tribunal to decide disputes should bring two distinct advantages to the user. The first is that decisions are made jointly by a panel of people who pool legal and other expert knowledge and are the better for that range of skills (Para 1.2). More recently the *Mental Health Review Tribunal Report* (Department of Health, 2002, p. 7) states that:

> *Each member of the tribunal is entitled to an equal voice on questions of law, procedure and substance. No decisions are reserved for any particular member. For example, the legal member alone is not entitled to decide matters of law and the medical member alone is not entitled to decide medical matters. All the members participate in the making of decisions and although the legal member is expected to draft and sign the written record, this is done only after taking into account the contributions of the other members.*

Given that the majority of hearings lasted longer than an hour and frequently involved complex and divergent information, it was surprising to find that in over two-thirds of tribunals the decision was reached and written within 15 minutes.

Contrary to the expectation that all members would contribute to decision-making, a number of deliberations were characterised by a complete lack of discussion, and decisions were reached and recorded under the sole influence of the tribunal president. Discussion of the evidence in the deliberation where it did occur was highly selective in terms of the evidence discussed and the issues raised.

In accordance with the rules of natural justice, the tribunal should examine the factual basis of the RMO's opinion. However, tribunals do not have powers of investigation, and they are limited to oral and written reports, the accuracy of which cannot always be ascertained. Over time, layers of information and misinformation are built into reports, and hearings do not afford the time to track these changes. Some RMOs seemed unaware of the legal significance of their evidence, and, occasionally, the veracity of RMO statements was challenged by patients and subsequently retracted by RMOs.

In reaching a decision, tribunal members are expected to apply the statutory criteria to the evidence they have heard. But this is a difficult and complex task because of the divergences of opinion, missing information and sometimes contradictory nature of the evidence. In order to make the process manageable, tribunal members adopted three types of strategy: identifying credible narratives, identifying credible witnesses, and substituting criteria for the statutory criteria. These 'rules of thumb' provided an alternative to the more intensive and time-consuming process of sifting through all the evidence and applying the fine detail of the Mental Health Act 1983.

Credible narratives and witnesses

Establishing a credible narrative involved little more than identifying plausible explanations. Credible narratives were usually established during the deliberation when there was no chance of acquiring additional information. Tribunal members frequently attributed suspect motives to witnesses when accounts did not 'add up' or seem plausible. Credible witnesses were those whose motives were beyond suspicion. Tribunal members seemed to operate within a normative framework in which psychiatrists were assumed to have the patient's best interests at heart. The evidence of patients, on the other hand, was felt to be less reliable through the effects of mental illness or the desire to be discharged.

Substitution of the statutory criteria

Given the difficulties experienced by tribunal members in applying the criteria for discharge it was not surprising to find that they developed a view of their task based on an analysis of what lay behind the intentions of the statutory criteria. The twin pillars of their role thus involved: balancing the patient's right to liberty against maximising the therapeutic outcome of treatment; and balancing the patient's rights against the protection of the public.

This balancing act reduced the need for a strict interpretation of the statutory criteria but involved the tribunal in predictions about how a patient would manage if discharged. As outlined in the previous section, the presence or absence of symptoms, of insight, of compliance and/or cooperation and of risk and danger to the patient and public were seen as the main relevant criteria.

Konecni and Ebbesen (1984), in their study of the way in which judges make decisions, reported that judges claimed to be responsive to one aspect of the Californian guidelines, while in practice their actual decisions were directly influenced by an entirely different consideration – that of perceived dangerousness:

> *It is impossible to estimate the extent to which beliefs held privately by judges, prosecutors, psychiatrists and other decision-makers about the factors that influence their decisions match what they publicly espouse in interviews, questionnaires and experiments etc.* [Konecni and Ebbesen, 1984]

In this study, members expressed a willingness to take risks. They recognised that theirs was a risky business: a patient discharged by a tribunal is discharged against the advice of their RMO. In practice, however, members were keen to identify the likelihood and the nature of an adverse outcome should a patient be discharged. In the deliberations, the benchmark against which risk was measured was the worst-case scenario – fear of the worst possible outcome. Myers (1997, p. 255) reports the existence of a logical principle that the more dire the possible consequences, the smaller the acceptable risk. There is also an illogical belief that the more dire these consequences are perceived to be, the greater the perceived risk. Myers concludes by saying that tribunals and RMOs may not be exempt from this phobic reasoning. Taylor and Monahan (1996) recognised that clinicians from all professional disciplines had a tendency to over-predict violence in psychiatric populations and it is possible that tribunal members are no different. However, if the fear of adverse consequences is allowed to replace thorough decision-making with all its attendant risks then, as the Aarvold Report highlights, there is a danger that patients will be detained longer than is necessary.

> *The complete elimination of any risk to the public could only be achieved by continuing to detain these patients perhaps indefinitely, long after many of them had recovered from their mental disorder, and for periods in excess of any term of imprisonment. We are sure that in our society this would be seen as an inhumane avoidance of the responsibility for making a proper judgement in each case.* [Aarvold Report, 1973]

Tribunals are often accused of putting the protection of the public before the patient's rights. This is not surprising, because a tribunal that does not discharge cannot be shown to have made the wrong decision. On the other hand, a tribunal discharge that results in an adverse event (rare though they may be) attracts publicity and criticism. However careful the assessment of the risks involved, some adverse events will occur: they do not necessarily demonstrate any error of judgement.

It is clear that there will always be a group of patients for whom it matters little whether the processes are good or poor. These are mainly patients who are obviously suffering extreme mental health conditions and exhibiting florid symptoms. These patients' cases will pass effortlessly through the decision-making process because the outcome will not depend on a rigorous assessment of the evidence. However, there are patients whose cases might benefit from a tighter, more rigorous application of due process. They are the cases where a stricter interpretation of the law might make the difference between detention and discharge.

(iv) Training

At the time this study was undertaken, training for members had been introduced. However, none of the members interviewed or observed in this study had received training prior to sitting as a tribunal member. They learned their skills on the job. The *Guide for Members* along with the Rules were seen as providing guidance, but there was little else. Little attempt was made after any tribunal to critically appraise the experience.

Over the last three years there has been a significant investment in the training of tribunal members as a way of ensuring greater uniformity of practice and procedure. According to the *Mental Health Review Tribunal Report 1999–2001* (Department of Health, 2002) newly appointed members are required to attend an induction course organised by the MHRT National Training Group before sitting on a panel to observe a series of case hearings. An analysis of training needs for experienced MHRT members completed in late 1998 has led to the development of a new three-year National Training Framework, and a comprehensive and authoritative *Training and Practice Manual* for use by all members is in preparation.

A new tribunal?

Since this study was carried out, plans for a new Mental Health Act have been published. The Government's White Paper 'Reforming the Mental Health Act 1983' was published in December 2000 and the draft Mental Health Bill was published in June 2002. The draft bill (2002) contains plans for revising the legal framework to take account of changes in mental health services, treatment and patterns of care. The reforms propose a new mental health tribunal with a new remit and composition.

The draft Mental Health Bill (2002) is underpinned by a single pathway for compulsory assessment, care and treatment based on three distinct stages:

(i) preliminary examination;
(ii) formal assessment and initial treatment;
(iii) care and treatment.

Decisions to begin assessment and initial treatment under compulsory powers will be based on a preliminary examination by two registered medical practitioners and an approved mental health professional who must agree that evidence exists to support all four conditions outlined in clause 6 and recorded as follows.

6 The relevant conditions

(1) In this Part, references to the relevant conditions are to the following conditions.

(2) The first condition is that the patient is suffering from mental disorder.

(3) The second condition is that that mental disorder is of such a nature or degree as to warrant the provision of medical treatment to him.

(4) The third condition is –

- (a) in the case of a patient who is at substantial risk of causing serious harm to other persons, that it is necessary for the protection of those persons that medical treatment be provided to him, and
- (b) in any other case, that –
  - (i) it is necessary for the health and safety of the patient or the protection of other persons that medical treatment be provided to him, and
  - (ii) that treatment cannot be provided to him unless he is subject to the provisions of this Act.

(5) The fourth condition is that appropriate medical treatment is available in the patient's case.

In addition, the examiners must also decide whether the patient needs to be detained in hospital for formal assessment or whether the assessment can be done whilst the patient remains in the community. If, following the preliminary examination, a decision is taken that assessment and initial treatment are required, the approved mental health professional will have to register the decision within 24 hours (clause 17(1)). In the second stage of the new procedures a patient will be given a full assessment of his or her health and social care needs and receive treatment set out in a formal care plan. This initial period of assessment and treatment under compulsory powers will be limited to a maximum of 28 days from the point at which the initial decision is registered.

A patient, or his/her nominated person[2], may request a tribunal review during this initial period of assessment and treatment. Rules to be made by the Lord Chancellor will specify the period within which tribunals must decide applications. At this stage in the process, the tribunal must discharge the patient if the four conditions for compulsion (clause 6) are not met. If the conditions for compulsory care are met the tribunal will be able to confirm the decision of the examiners and either accept or amend the conditions under which the assessment is to be carried out. It will also be able to make a care and treatment order (clause 38) for up to six months, or extend the original period of assessment for a period of up to 28 days (clause 40).

In one of the major changes in legislation the clinical supervisor must apply to the new mental health tribunal to continue compulsory care and treatment beyond 28 days. The application to the tribunal will have to include: a copy of the care plan; the reasons for the clinical supervisor's decision that all the conditions for compulsory care are met; a description of the patient's mental disorder for which medical treatment is proposed; a description of any other proposed treatment; and details of requirements to be imposed where the patient will be non-resident. The tribunal will be able to make an initial care and treatment order for up to six months. Where a patient is subject to an order authorising medical treatment that covers a period of three months or more, clause 42 makes provision for a patient, or his nominated person acting on his behalf, to apply to the tribunal for the order to be discharged. The tribunal must consider whether all the conditions continue to exist for compulsory care (clause 6).

At the time this research was undertaken the onus was on the patient to prove to the tribunal that he or she satisfied the s. 72 criteria for discharge. In a case taken to the Court of Appeal in 2001 (see Chapter 2) the burden of proof was reversed[3]. The draft Mental Health Bill (Department of Health, 2002a) proposes that the clinical supervisor must demonstrate that there is a need for compulsory powers. This brings the legislation into line with the ECHR ruling (*R.* (on the application of H) v. *Mental Health Review Tribunal, North and East London Region* [2001] H.R.L.R. 36).

Composition

The new tribunal will also differ significantly in the role of its members. The mental health tribunal will have a legally qualified chair, a clinical member (someone appointed by the Lord Chancellor who has knowledge or experience of the treatment of mentally disordered persons) and a general member (someone appointed by the Lord Chancellor who has knowledge or experience of the provision of mental health services). In this study, although lay members were required to have 'knowledge of the social services, social administration or other appropriate experience' (*A Guide for Members*, 1996b) they did not participate to the same extent as the medical and legal members in the decision-making process. It is difficult to assess on the basis of this study whether replacing the lay member with a member with experience of mental health services will give rise to more active participation in the discussions in the deliberation, since many of the lay members in this study did have relevant mental health experience.

The medical member role, as it existed under the 1983 Act, and at the time this study was undertaken, has been abandoned. Instead, when the clinical supervisor applies to the tribunal for authority to continue compulsory care and treatment beyond 28 days, arrangements will be made for the patient to be seen by an independent doctor drawn from a panel of people appointed to provide expert evidence to the tribunal. This panel will include doctors specialising in different areas, for example old age, child and forensic psychiatry. It is envisaged that there will be some matching of the area of expertise to the patient. The medical adviser will prepare a report for the tribunal dealing with the merits of the application and commenting on the matters set out in the application (clause 48). The expert panel will also include people with experience in social care, nursing, and probation. This expert independent panel removes the tensions that currently exist under the 1983 Act in the dual role of the medical member as fact-finder and decision-maker.

Process

The new mental health tribunal will have more flexible powers in relation to the care and management of the patient under compulsion as long as the conditions for compulsion continue to exist. In particular, the new mental health tribunal will have the power to amend the care plan submitted by the patient's clinical supervisor and the conditions under which medical treatment can be given. It is not clear within the draft bill how the tribunal will enforce these new powers, nor how the clinical supervisor may respond to what might be seen as outside interference.

Under the 1983 Mental Health Act, MHRTs discharged few patients from section. However, hearings frequently offered an opportunity for indirectly improving the therapeutic outcomes for the patient. The hearing allowed the patient's treatment and progress to be examined in detail by a group of people not connected with the hospital and provided patients with a controlled setting in which they could talk to their RMO through an advocate. The plans outlined above build on some of the strengths of tribunals and have the potential to ensure that care and treatment is provided under the most suitable conditions.

While the overarching framework within which tribunals operate will change, the task of the tribunal remains to decide on the basis of evidence put to it whether the conditions for continuing care and treatment under compulsory powers are met. Whether the tribunal conducts its business through an oral hearing or through a paper-based exercise the same challenges arise in relation to decision-making. The draft bill (2002) makes reference to a new code of practice to be published by the appropriate minister and the need for the Lord Chancellor to draft Rules for the conduct and operation of tribunals and these are clearly necessary. However, in order to ensure that decision-making is consistent and fair there will be a need to make considerable investment in the training of all those involved in the new tribunal and effective monitoring of the new legislation.

Future decision-making

MHRT decision-making involves the synthesis of a large and complicated body of medical and social information, some of which may be divergent or incomplete or inaccurate. The skills required to assess accurately the merits of this information are wide-ranging and time-consuming, making decision-making with a high degree of certainty almost impossible within the tribunal system as it existed at the time of the research. The scheduling of three or four tribunals in a day, frequently at other locations, is not conducive to good decision-making.

Not surprisingly, therefore, members in this study developed labour-saving devices to make the task more manageable. In this they were responding to the ethos of the tribunal system and the realities of the implementation of policy. We have seen that they adopted decision-making strategies which involved structuring evidence around an outcome, which created the circumstances in which early or provisional conclusions, however misleading, were influential.

The new legislation makes some significant changes to the operation of tribunals:

(i) most notably a more coherent pathway through the process of compulsory detention;
(ii) the removal of the medical member role as a fact-finder and decision-maker;
(iii) the European Convention-compliant requirement that the clinical supervisor makes a case for detention rather than the onus being on the patient to prove that the criteria for discharge are satisfied; and
(iv) allowing evidence from the patient to be presented alongside that of the medical experts.

But are these changes radical enough to counter some of the problems identified in our study? There must be concerns that new tensions may emerge as a result of creating a tribunal which is responsible for both authorising and reviewing compulsory care and treatment. Will tribunals have more difficulty discharging a patient from section if it is as a result of their decision that they were detained in the first place? Further, the extent to which the new panel of experts will draw on the current pool of Mental Health Review Tribunal members is also not known. Clearly, if the membership does not change there may be a danger that the flaws of the Mental Health Review Tribunal persist in the new tribunal. On the other hand, staff shortages in psychiatry and nursing may restict the pool from which new members may be drawn. The criteria to be considered by the tribunal in determining the need for compulsory care continue to centre on two concepts – the 'nature' or 'degree' of mental disorder – which tribunal members under the 1983 Act found difficult to interpret and apply. Unless some work is done to clarify these concepts and provide operational definitions, the same problems with inconsistent interpretations will apply.

Eastman (1994, p. 43) states that civil rights are granted by law but effected by resources. There can be no doubt that considerable resources will need to be invested in the training of members and in the monitoring of tribunals to ensure that they are consistent and fair.

Currently, tribunals are least effective in those very situations in which they have most to contribute. From this study it is clear that good decision-making and due process should go hand in hand. This includes recognising the importance of the nature and type of evidence presented to tribunals and the criteria they are asked to apply to that evidence. To interpret the evidence, members need good research evidence on diagnostic and treatment pathways, and on risk and the prediction of violence. They also need clear operational definitions against which they can examine the evidence; and they need the time and resources to examine properly and weigh the evidence that they hear. They need opportunities to meet and discuss cases and they need constructive feedback on the factors they are taking into account. These cannot be legislated for, but are vital if the new Mental Health Tribunal is to perform better than its predecessor.

Notes

1 Walker-Smith, Minister of Health, reported in Hansard, col. 713 (26 January 1959).

2 The nominated person replaces the patient's nearest relative in the 1983 Act. Different arrangements will apply according to the age of the patient and their capacity to choose who they wish to be their nominated person.

3 Although the government had the option of amending the law in line with this landmark ruling, the overhaul of the Mental Health Act 1983 was already underway, making it unlikely that remedial action would be taken using the section 10 fast track procedures. So, while tribunals must apply the reverse burden of proof, the 1983 Act will continue to contravene the Convention until the new Mental Health Act is enacted.

Appendix 1

Pilot Study Statistics

A total of 21 tribunals were sampled by the tribunal regional offices for researchers to observe. For the reasons outlined below only eight tribunals were observed.

Cancellations

Seven tribunals were cancelled. Three were cancelled on the day.

Adjournments

Four tribunals were adjourned before they had even started and one tribunal was suspended when the president discovered that the section papers had been incorrectly completed. According to the tribunal president, this invalidated the patient's detention, rendering a tribunal hearing redundant.

Other reasons

One tribunal could not be located in the hospital; none of the staff working in the hospital could identify its location.

Of the eight tribunals observed, not all were observed in their entirety. In three tribunals, researchers were denied access to observe the deliberation.

Appendix 2

Tribunal Observations

Patient identifier:
Pre-hearing meeting

Start time: End time:

People present at pre-hearing meeting:
medical tribunal member
legal tribunal member
lay tribunal member
tribunal clerk

Patient characteristics

1. SEX: Male Female
2. Ethnicity
3. Age
4. Diagnosis
5. Medication
6. Does patient have any history?:
   a) Attempted/actual violence
   b) Attempted/actual self-harm

Tribunal

7. Length of time of current detention:
8. Status of hearing: application
   automatic referral
9. Previous applications to tribunal, if known (date, outcome):

Information/reports circulated
(tick)
responsible medical officer
medical tribunal member
approved social worker
independent psychiatrist
independent social worker

Layout of venue

Start time: End time:

People present at hearing:
medical tribunal member
legal tribunal member
lay tribunal member
tribunal clerk
legal representative
responsible medical officer
approved social worker
independent psychiatrist
independent social worker
other ....

Deliberation

Start time: End time:

People present at deliberation:
(tick)
medical tribunal member
legal tribunal member
lay tribunal member
tribunal clerk
Other ....

Venue (layout if different)

Outcome?
discharge immediately
delayed discharge
no discharge

Formal reasons given for decision?

After-care arrangements
s 117 meetings
appointment of key worker

How is decision to be communicated to patient?

Appendix 3

Topic Guide

DECISION-MAKING IN
MENTAL HEALTH REVIEW TRIBUNALS

Policy Studies Institute
January 1997

Interviewer ....
Date ....
Time ....
Region ....
Type of tribunal member ....
Identifier ....

Identifier ....

Mental Health Review Tribunals
Interviews with tribunal members

Purpose of interview – (to find out more about processes of hearing and deliberations and to identify issues and themes around decision-making)

NB Section 2, 3 and 37 non-restricted patients.

I'd like to begin by asking you for some background details about yourself

1. Background

1. How long have you been a tribunal member?
2. How many tribunals do you sit on in a week/month?
3. Why did you become a tribunal member?
   PROBE: previous work experience
4. In your opinion what are the roles of the three tribunal members?
   PROBE: In what ways do their roles differ from yours?

5. How relevant is your previous personal experience for your role on the tribunal?
   PROBE: In what ways is it relevant?

2. Training/induction

6. Did you receive any training before you became a member?
   If yes

6a. What did this entail?
   PROBE: Is your training regularly updated?

7. Do you feel that your training prepared you for your role as a tribunal member?
   PROBE: knowledge of the mental health act/ knowledge about medical and legal issues (case law?)
   PROBE: In what ways did it prepare you?
   PROBE: In what ways did it not prepare you for your role?
   PROBE: Would you have liked more training? If yes, what sort?
   PROBE: Have you had ongoing training? If yes, what sort and when?
   If no training

8. Would you have liked some training?
   PROBE: Nature and type of training

9. Do you do other work in addition to your tribunal work?
   If yes
   What is this work?

3. Hearing

I'd like next to talk about the actual process of the tribunal

10. What in your opinion are the major differences between section 2 and section 3 hearings?

11a. What do you do with the reports when you get them through the post?
   PROBE: Do have any kind of working method?

11b. In your view how valuable is the pre-hearing members' meeting?
   PROBE: Why?
   Ordering of evidence?

12. What do you think are the advantages and disadvantages to a patient of being legally represented at a tribunal?

13. In general, how useful do you find the information supplied by different witnesses?
   PROBE: In turn go through:
      Responsible Medical Officer
      Social worker
      Nurse
      Family
      Friends
      Patient
   PROBE: for difference between reports and oral evidence

4. Evidence

14a. Are different styles of 'examination' better than others (*inquisitorial versus adversarial*)?

14b What are the advantages/disadvantages of taking evidence from the patient first?

14c. What are the advantages/disadvantages of taking evidence from the patient last?

15. How easy do you find it to establish the accuracy of information or evidence you are given?

5. Statutory criteria and decision-making

16. What information do you draw on when making your assessment of whether or not a patient should be discharged?
PROBE: Evidence, others' opinions, personal experience
PROBE: Which evidence is the most important?
PROBE: Which evidence is less important?

17. In your opinion what are the most important considerations when making a decision to discharge a patient from section?
PROBE: only if they ask what like: Role of compliance, prior periods of leave, family support?

18. In what sort of circumstances would you use discretionary powers to discharge a patient?

19a. To what extent do the statutory criteria provide a useful framework by which to examine the evidence?

19b How do you interpret the 'nature' of a mental illness in the criteria – 'of a nature or degree which makes it appropriate for a patient to be liable to be detained in hospital for assessment or medical treatment'?
PROBE: Characteristics of nature

20. Have there been any occasions on which you've felt that you did not have enough information on which to make a decision?
PROBE: What were the circumstances, what information was missing and what did you do?

21. How often is there conflicting evidence?
PROBE: What kinds of conflicting evidence – medical/social/legal?

22. How do you deal with conflicting evidence?
PROBE:

23. Are there any instances you can recall when you disagreed with the opinion of other members?
PROBE: for accounts of particular circumstances

24. How are differences of opinion/disagreements among tribunal members resolved?

6. Outcomes

25. Do you ever get to know what happens to the patients you discharge?
PROBE: level of knowledge about after-care programmes ? Would they like to know?
If yes
Identify how they got to hear about outcomes and from whom they heard
26. What about patients you don't discharge?
PROBE:
27. In general, what factors do you think influence the outcomes for a patient discharged from section?
PROBE: Compliance, availability of services etc.
28. Do you think the tribunal system works equally well for all types of patient?
PROBE: In what circumstances?
PROBE: Why, for which types does it work well?
PROBE: Why, for which types does it not work well?

7. Future of tribunals

29. What impact, if any, do the changes in health care delivery and in particular the availability of beds and resources for people with mental health problems have on tribunals?
30. In your opinion, does the current legislative framework adequately cover the remit of mental health review tribunals?
PROBE: Supervised discharge?
31. Is there anything about the tribunal process you would like to see changed?
If they ask – what like or for instance? PROBE: Resources
If yes
What?

Interviewer notes

The names for these interviews were supplied by tribunal office.

Confidentiality:	Anonymity of all respondents and regions from which drawn Data only used by the research team, individual interviews will not be discussed with regional chairmen or anyone else We are interested in their personal views and opinions

Interviewer comments on interview and interview schedule

Sex of respondent:

Length of interview
Content
Gaps
Logical progression and internal consistency
Other comments

Appendix 4

Extract from *Guide for Members* (1996b)

APPENDIX III (i)
ROLE OF REGIONAL CHAIRMAN

The principal functions of the Regional Chairman are as follows:

1. To be responsible for the administration of the Tribunal for his region in conjunction with the staff of the Tribunal office. The Tribunal Clerks for the Regions are on the establishment of the Department of Health. They are answerable to the Regional Chairman for the administration of the Tribunal but management responsibility for their actions lies with the Department.
2. To appoint members for particular Tribunal hearings and to appoint a deputy to act for him if for any reason he is unable to act himself.
3. To exercise, or delegate the exercise of, the powers of the Tribunal as regards preliminary and incidental matters and to give such directions as he thinks fit to ensure the speedy and just determination of both applications and references.
4. To preside at a variety of Tribunal hearings so as to acquire a broad experience of members and current issues.
5. To provide guidance to members whenever appropriate on preliminary and incidental matters, hearing procedures, including decision making, manner of questioning of witnesses and good practice generally.
6. In co-operation with the staff of the Tribunal office to organise meetings, conferences and training for members.
7. To interview candidates for membership, to assess their suitability and to advise the Department of Health/Lord Chancellor's Department accordingly.
8. To advise the Department of Health/Lord Chancellor's Department on the suitability of members for re-appointment. In cases of doubt to interview the members concerned and discuss any shortcomings with them.
9. To monitor the performance and usage of members in his region for example by attending Tribunal hearings as an observer.
10. To meet other Regional Chairmen regularly in order to devise and agree national policies. (Since each Regional Chairman is autonomous the only existing machinery for formulating and implementing national policies is by

way of discussion and agreement at Regional Chairmen's meetings.)

11. As necessary to liaise with other agencies (e.g. health authorities, NHS Trusts, Law Society) and provide information on practical and procedural matters.

APPENDIX III (ii)
ROLE OF LEGAL MEMBER

The legal member is the President of the tribunal. He should be fully conversant with the Mental Health Act 1983 and the Mental Health Review Tribunal Rules 1983 so that he should be able readily to recognise practical problems, including problems of conflict of interest, privacy of proceedings, disclosure of documents, and exclusion and is aware of the need to avoid inappropriate formality in the proceedings. His principal functions are as follows:

1. To read any papers received from the Tribunal office prior to the hearing. If necessary to discuss with the Tribunal office the need for any additional reports or information, and where appropriate to seek a direction from the Regional Chairman.
2. To take the chair at the hearing and to advise the other members of the tribunal on matters of law, especially with regard to the Tribunal's powers and to the application of the statutory criteria. Presidents should note that no decisions are reserved to them by the Rules and that each member is entitled to an equal voice on matters of law, procedure and substance.
3. To meet the other members of the Tribunal approximately half an hour before the commencement of the actual hearing in order to discuss and agree preliminary matters. These may include questions of privacy, disclosure, and evidence; and, if appropriate, which of the Tribunal members should lead the questioning of particular witnesses. This period also provides an opportunity for the Tribunal to identify the likely issues, and the medical member, who will already have seen the patient, will probably have a good idea of what they are likely to be and of any difficulties which might affect the patient's ability to give evidence. However, it is not usually appropriate to ask the medical member his opinion of the patient's mental condition at this stage.
4. At the commencement of the actual hearing, to introduce the members of the Tribunal to the patient and to other persons present and to explain that they are independent people unconnected with the hospital (and, in restricted cases, unconnected with the Home Office). He must also explain the manner of proceeding which the Tribunal proposes to adopt and, in appropriate cases, the Tribunal's powers. It may be helpful if he asks the patient, or the legal representative, at the outset what it is the Tribunal is being asked to do. So far as is possible this should be done in an informal manner designed to put the patient at ease. The manner in which the patient wishes to be addressed should also be established and it should not be assumed that the use of patient's forename will be acceptable.

5. To ensure that the proceedings are conducted in a fair and judicial manner, avoiding inappropriate formality, excessive length and generally seeing that the Tribunal is managed well. This will include giving the other members of the Tribunal, the patient (or the patient's legal representative) and the RMO the opportunity to question each of the witnesses. It will be necessary to bear in mind that it would a breach of a fundamental requirement of natural justice for the Tribunal to decide on a basis known only to itself and, accordingly, where the medical member's opinion of the patient's mental condition differs significantly from that of the RMO (and/or from any other medical evidence presented to the tribunal), this must be brought into the open in the course of questioning at the hearing. The President should try to ensure that all questions, however searching, are asked in a polite and courteous manner and that the hearing is conducted, so far as possible, in a way that does not undermine the relationship between the patient and the RMO.
6. To take a note of the proceedings.
7. At the conclusion of the evidence, to ensure that the members of the Tribunal together deliberate on all relevant matters in addressing the statutory criteria and reaching the Tribunal's decision. Once the decision has been agreed the President should draft the reasons therefor, taking into account the contribution of the other members, and should record and sign the decision which has been reached. The language used should be clear and straightforward so as to be readily understood by the patient. In the event of disagreement, the decision is by a majority.
8. To inform the patient how and when the decision will be communicated to him.

APPENDIX III (iii)
ROLE OF MEDICAL MEMBER

The medical member's principal functions are as follows:

1. Having arranged an appointment for the purpose, to conduct a preliminary examination of the patient prior to the hearing and to take such steps as he considers necessary to form an opinion of the patient's mental condition. These steps should include reference to hospital documentation and discussions with hospital staff.
2. To inform the Tribunal office of any potential problems arising out of the preliminary examination which might affect the hearing procedures, and if necessary refer back to the Regional Chairman on any matter which he believes requires a preliminary decision.
3. To advise the Tribunal office, at its request, with regard to the withdrawal of applications, the need for legal representation and similar matters. To inform the Tribunal office if he discovers at the preliminary examination that the patient is not legally represented.

4. To consider the possibility of any conflict of interest arising from any former contact with the patient and to notify the Tribunal office accordingly. If the preliminary examination takes place on the day of the hearing, and the medical member considers that the patient is not well enough for the hearing to go ahead, he should inform the other members so that they can decide what action to take.
5. To report to the other members of the Tribunal, when requested, on his preliminary examination and to advise on and explain medical terminology and technicalities as necessary.
6. To meet the other members of the Tribunal approximately half an hour before the commencement of the actual hearing in order to discuss and agree preliminary matters, the order in which the witnesses should give evidence and, if appropriate, which of the Tribunal members should lead the questioning of particular witnesses.

   This period also provides an opportunity for the Tribunal to identify the likely issues, and the medical member, having already seen the patient, will probably have a good idea of what they are likely to be and of any difficulties which might affect the patient's ability to give evidence. However, it is usually inappropriate for the medical member to give his opinion of the patient's mental condition at this stage.
7. To put such questions to each of the witnesses who give evidence at the hearing as he considers relevant. In particular, the medical member may consider it appropriate to question the RMO in relation to the patient's history, progress, treatment, prognosis and future care, although he must bear in mind that the hearing is neither a seminar nor a case conference. In appropriate cases he may lead the questioning of the RMO if this has been agreed beforehand with the other members of the Tribunal. However, he must appreciate that he performs a dual role at the Tribunal as a fact-finder and as a decision maker and it is therefore essential that his opinion of the patient's mental condition, if it differs significantly from that of RMO, should be made known to everyone present in the course of his questioning. Thus a situation will be avoided where the members of the Tribunal are acting on the basis of evidence known only to themselves, which would, of course, be a breach of a fundamental principle of natural justice and likely to invalidate the decision.
8. At the conclusion of the evidence, to participate in the members' discussion so as to enable a decision to be reached (if necessary by a majority) and to contribute as appropriate to the drafting of the record of the decision and of the reasons therefore.

APPENDIX III (iv)
ROLE OF LAY MEMBER

The lay member's principal functions are as follows:

1. To acquire a basic understanding of the legal framework determining detention, discharge and the powers of the Tribunal. Some knowledge of the health and social services systems is also essential.
2. To read and consider any papers received from the Tribunal office prior to the hearing with a view to ascertaining the main features of the patient's history and reasons for his detention. It may also be possible to identify the main issues which seem likely to arise at the hearing.
3. To consider the possibility of any conflict of interest due to any former contact with the patient and to notify the Tribunal office or, as the case may be, the other Tribunal members accordingly.
4. To meet the other members of the Tribunal approximately half an hour before the commencement of the actual hearing in order to discuss and agree on preliminary matters, the order in which witnesses should give evidence, and, if appropriate, which of the Tribunal members should lead the questioning of particular witnesses. This period also provides an opportunity for the tribunal to identify the likely issues. The medical member, having already seen the patient, will probably have a good idea of what they are likely to be and of any difficulties which might affect the patient's ability to give evidence. However, it is usually inappropriate for the medical member to give his opinion of the patient's mental condition at this stage.
5. To put such questions to each of the witnesses who give evidence at the hearing as may be relevant and, in appropriate cases, to lead the questioning of the social worker if this has been agreed beforehand with the other members of the Tribunal.
6. At the conclusion of the evidence, to participate in the discussion with the other members of the Tribunal so as to enable a decision to be reached (if necessary by a majority) and to contribute as appropriate to the drafting of the record of the decisions and the reasons therefor. In reaching such a decision the lay member is entitled to an equal voice with the other members of the Tribunal on all questions of law, procedure and substance.

Appendix 5

DECISION FORM S72(1)(a) – Unrestricted Patient S2

MENTAL HEALTH ACT 1983
MENTAL HEALTH TRIBUNAL RULES 1983
DECISION OF MENTAL HEALTH REVIEW TRIBUNAL

.... REGION

IN RESPECT OF AN APPLICATION DATED:

....

1. NAME OF PATIENT: ....

2. NAME AND ADDRESS OF HOSPITAL:

....

....

....

....

3. DECISION OF THE TRIBUNAL:
   (a) The patient **SHALL** be discharged from liability to be detained with effect
   From: ....

   OR

   (b) The patient **SHALL NOT** be discharged.

THE LEGAL GROUNDS FOR THE TRIBUNAL'S DECISION:

*The Tribunal is obliged to discharge the patient if the answer to either of the following questions is "**YES**"*

4. THE LEGAL GROUNDS FOR THE TRIBUNAL'S DECISION
The tribunal is obliged to discharge the patient if the answer to either of the following questions is "YES".

Question	Decision of the Tribunal
A. Is the Tribunal satisfied that the patient is not now suffering from mental disorder or from degree which warrants the patient's detention in a hospital for assessment (or for assessment followed by medical treatment) for at least a limited period?	**YES/NO**
B. Is the Tribunal satisfied that the patient's detention as aforesaid is not justified in the interests of the patient's own health or safety or with a view to the protection of other persons?	**YES/NO**

5. DOES THE TRIBUNAL CONSIDER THAT THIS IS A CASE WHERE IT IS APPROPRIATE TO DISCHARGE THE PATIENT UNDER DISCRETIONARY POWERS?
YES/NO

6. RECOMMENDATIONS PURSUANT TO SECTION 72(3) (if any):

....

....

....

....

REASONS FOR THE TRIBUNAL'S DECISION AND RECOMMENDATIONS:

....

....

....

....

....

....

....

....

Signed: ....
(President)

Date: ....

DECISION FORM S72(1)(b) – Unrestricted Patient S3, S37

MENTAL HEALTH ACT 1983
MENTAL HEALTH TRIBUNAL RULES 1983
DECISION OF MENTAL HEALTH REVIEW TRIBUNAL

.... REGION

IN RESPECT OF AN APPLICATION/REFERENCE DATED:

....

1. NAME OF PATIENT:

   ....

2. NAME AND ADDRESS OF HOSPITAL:

   ....

   ....

   ....

   ....

3. SECTION OF THE ACT UNDER WHICH THE PATIENT IS LIABLE TO BE DETAINED: S3/S37

4. DECISION OF THE TRIBUNAL:
   (a) The patient **SHALL** be discharged from liability to be detained with effect from: ....

   OR

   (b) The patient **SHALL NOT** be discharged.

5. (a) If the patient is not discharged, does the Tribunal re-classify? **YES/NO**
   (b) if "YES" namely:
   from .... to ....
   (See 9)

6. THE LEGAL GROUNDS FOR THE TRIBUNAL'S DECISION:
The Tribunal is obliged to discharge the patient if the answer to either of the following questions is "**YES**"

Question	Decision of the Tribunal
A. Is the Tribunal satisfied that the patient is not now suffering from mental illness, psychopathic disorder, severe mental impairment, mental impairment or from any of those forms of disorder of a nature or degree which makes it appropriate for the patient to be liable to be detained in a hospital for medical treatment?	**YES/NO**
B. Is the Tribunal satisfied that it is not necessary for the health or safety of the patient or for the protection of others that the patient should receive such treatment?	**YES/NO**

7. If the answers to both questions at 6 (A) and (B) above are "NO", does the Tribunal consider that this is a case where it is appropriate to discharge the patient under its discretionary powers? **YES/NO**

In reaching its conclusions above the Tribunal has had regard to:

(a) the likelihood of medical treatment alleviating or preventing a deterioration of the patient's condition, **AND**

(b) the likelihood of the patient, if suffering from mental illness or severe mental impairment, if discharged, being able to care for her/himself, to obtain the care she/he needs, or to guard her/himself against serious exploitation.

8. RECOMMENDATION:
With a view to facilitating his discharge on a future date, does the Tribunal recommend that the patient be –

a) granted leave of absence from the hospital? **YES/NO**
b) transferred to another hospital? **YES/NO**
c) transferred into guardship? **YES/NO**

If the answer to any of the above is "YES" will the Tribunal consider his/her case further in the event of such recommendation not being complied with? **YES/NO**
If the answer to the question above is "YES", the Tribunal will consider the case further on: Date: ………………..

9. THE REASONS FOR THE TRIBUNAL'S DECISION AND RECOMMENDATIONS
(including re-classification, if appropriate):

....

....

....

....

....

....

....

....

....

....

....

....

....

....

....

....

....

....

....

....

....

....

....

....

Signed: ....
(President)

Date: ....

References

Aarvold Report (1973) Report on the *Review of Procedures for the Discharge and Supervision of Psychiatric Patients Subject to Special Restrictions*. Cmnd 5191 London: HMSO.

Adler, P. and Adler, P. (1994) 'Observational techniques'. In *Collecting and Interpreting Qualitative Materials*, eds K. Denzin and Y. Lincoln, pp. 79–109. Thousand Oaks: Sage.

The Annual Report of the Council on Tribunals 1982–1983 (1983) London: HMSO.

Appleby, L., Shaw, J., Amos, T. *et al.* (1999) 'Suicide within 12 months of contact with mental health services: national clinical survey'. *British Medical Journal*, 8 May, 318, pp. 1235–9.

Asch, S. (1956) 'Studies of independence and conformity: I. A minority of one against a unanimous majority'. *Psychological Monographs: General and Applied*, 70 (9), pp. 1–70.

Atkinson, P. and Hammersley, M. (1998) 'Ethnography and participant observation'. In *Strategies of Qualitative Inquiry*, eds, K. Denzin and Y. Lincoln, pp. 110–32. Thousand Oaks: Sage.

Audit Commission (Goldberg and Huxley) (1994) *Finding a Place. A Review of Mental Health Services for Adults*. London: HMSO.

Barnes, M. (1996) 'Citizens in detention: the role of the Mental Health Act Commission in protecting the rights of detained patients'. *Local Government Studies*, Autumn, 22 (3), pp. 28–46.

Bean, P. (1996) *Mental Disorder and Legal Control*. Cambridge: Cambridge University Press.

Bebbington, P. (1996) 'The economic significance of social factors influencing the outcome of schizophrenia'. *Handbook of Mental Health Economics and Health Policy* 1, pp. 65–78.

Benson, P. (1994) 'Deinstitutionalization and Family Caretaking of the Seriously Mentally Ill'. *International Journal of Law and Psychiatry*, 17 (2), pp. 119–38.

Bjork, R. (1972) 'Theoretical implications of directed forgetting'. In *Coding Processes in Human Memory*, eds, A. Melton and E. Martin, pp. 217–35. Washington DC: Winston.

Bjorkly, S. (1997) 'Clinical assessment of dangerousness in psychotic patients: some risk indicators and pitfalls'. *Aggression and Violent Behavior*, 2 (2), pp. 167–78.

Blumenthal, S. and Wessely, S. (1994) *The Pattern of Delays in Mental Health Review Tribunals (summary)*. London: HMSO.

Bower, B. (1995) 'Law and disorders'. *Science News*, 147, pp. 8–10.

British Medical Association (1995) *Assessment of Mental Capacity*. London: British Medical Association.

Brockman, B. (1993) 'Preparing for Mental Health Review Tribunals: reports and dilemmas'. *Psychiatric Bulletin*, 17, pp. 544–7.
Burn, R. (1814) *The Justice of the Peace and Parish Officer.* London: Butterworth.
Campbell, T. and Heginbotham, C. (1991) *Mental Illness: Prejudice, Discrimination and the Law.* Aldershot: Dartmouth Publishing.
Carson, J., Holloway, F., Oliver, N. *et al.* (1996) 'Quality of life, community care and the severely mentally ill'. *Health and Social Care in the Community*, 4 (5), pp. 308–10.
Casper, J. and Benedict, K. (1993) The influence of outcome information and attitudes on juror decision making in search and seizure cases. In *Inside the Juror: The Psychology of Juror Decision Making* ed. R. Hastie pp. 65–83. Cambridge: Cambridge University Press.
Chicago tradition. London: Routledge.
Chiswick, D. (1996) 'Sentencing mentally disordered offenders'. *British Medical Journal*, 14 December, 313, pp. 1497–8.
Coid, J. (1996) 'Dangerous patients with mental illness: increased risks warrant new policies, adequate resources, and appropriate legislation'. *British Medical Journal*, 13 April, 312, pp. 965–9.
Cotterrell, R. (1984) *The Sociology of Law: An Introduction.* London: Butterworths.
Council on Tribunals (1983) *Annual Report of the Council on Tribunals 1982–3,* London: HMSO.
Crimlisk, H. and Phelan, M. (1996) 'Mental Health Review Tribunals'. *British Journal of Psychiatry*, 169, pp. 678–81.
Crepaz-Kay, D. (1994) 'I wish to register a complaint…' *Openmind*, 71 October/November, p. 5.
Council on Tribunals (2000) *Mental Health Review Tribunals: Special Report*. London: Council on Tribunals.
Davies, S., Thornicroft, G., Leese, M. *et al.* (1996) 'Ethnic differences in risk of compulsory psychiatric admission among representative cases of psychosis in London'. *British Medical Journal*, 2 March, 312, pp. 533–7.
Denzin, K. and Lincoln, Y. (eds) (1998a) *The Landscape of Qualitative Research.* Thousand Oaks: Sage.
Denzin, K. and Lincoln, Y. (eds) (1998b) *Strategies of Qualitative Inquiry.* Thousand Oaks: Sage.
Denzin, K. and Lincoln, Y. (eds) (1998c) *Collecting and Interpreting Qualitative Materials* Thousand Oaks: Sage.
Department of Health (1995) *Mental Health (Patients in the Community) Act 1995.* Chapter 5. London: HMSO.
Department of Health (1996a) *Mental Health Review Tribunals for England and Wales. Annual Report 1996*. London: Department of Health.
Department of Health (1996b) *Mental Health Review Tribunals in England and Wales. A Guide for Members*. London: Department of Health.
Department of Health, (1998) *Modernising Mental Health Services*. London: Department of Health.
Department of Health (1998a) *L* v. *Bournewood Community and Mental Health NHS Trust*. *Health Service Circular*, 10 July, HSC 1998/122.
Department of Health (1998b) *In-patients Formally Detained in Hospitals under the Mental Health Act 1983 and Other Legislation, England: 1987–88 and 1992–93 and 1997–98*. Statistical bulletin, November, pp. 1–23.
Department of Health (1999) *Reform of the Mental Health Act 1983*. London: The Stationery Office, Cm 4480.

Department of Health (1999a) *Mental Health National Service Framework*. London: Department of Health.
Department of Health (1999b) *Reform of the Mental Health Act 1983*. London: TSO, Cm 4480.
Department of Health (2000) *Reforming the Mental Health Act 1983*. London: The Stationery Office, Cm 5016-I.
Department of Health (2002) *Mental Health Review Tribunal Report. April 1999 to March 2001*. London: Department of Health.
Department of Health (2002a) *Draft Mental Health Bill*. London: The Stationery Office, Cm 5538-I.
Department of Health (2002b) *Draft Mental Health Bill. Explanatory Notes*. London: The Stationery Office, Cm 5538-II.
DHSS (1960) *Mental Health Act 1959: Memorandum on Parts I, IV–VIII and IX*. London: HMSO.
Donnelly, L. (1999) 'Standard issue'. *Health Service Journal*, 14 October, pp. 11–12.
Dowie, J. and Elstein, A. (eds) (1988) *Professional Judgment*. Cambridge: Cambridge University Press.
Eastman, N. (1984) 'Mental health law: civil liberties and the principle of reciprocity'. *British Medical Journal*, 1 January, 308, pp. 43–5.
Eastman, N. (1992) 'Psychiatric, psychological and legal models of man'. *International Journal of Law and Psychiatry*, 15, pp. 157–69.
Eastman, N. (1994) 'Mental health law: civil liberties and the principle of reciprocity'. *British Medical Journal*, 1 January, 308, pp. 43–5.
Eastman, N. and Peay, J. (eds) (1999) *Law without Enforcement*. Oxford: Hart.
Eldergill, A. (1998) *Mental Health Review Tribunals*. London: Sweet & Maxwell.
Ellsworth, P. (1993) 'Some steps between attitudes and verdicts'. In *Inside the Juror*. Ed. R. Hastie, pp. 42–65. Cambridge: Cambridge University Press.
Erikson, K. (1967) 'A comment on disguised observation in sociology'. *Social Problems*, 14, pp. 366–73.
Fasschnach, G. (1982) *Theory and Practice of Observing Behaviour.* London: Academic Press.
Fennell, P. (1977) 'The Mental Health Review Tribunal: a question of imbalance'. *British Journal of Law and Society*, 2, pp. 186–219.
Fennell, P. (1996) *Treatment without Consent*. London: Routledge.
Fisher, N., Turner, S., Pugh, R. and Taylor, C. (1994) 'Estimating numbers of homeless and homeless mentally ill people in north east Westminster by using capture-recapture analysis'. *British Medical Journal*, 1 January, 308, pp. 27–30.
Ford, F., Ryan, P., Beadsmoore, A. *et al.* (1997a) 'Intensive case management for people with serious mental illness – Site 2: clinical and social outcome'. *Journal of Medical Health*, 6 (2), pp. 181–90.
Ford, F., Ryan, P., Beadsmoore, A. *et al.* (1997b) 'Intensive case management for people with serious mental illness – Site 2: cost effectiveness'. *Journal of Medical Health*, 6 (2), pp. 191–9.
Foucault, M. (1986) *The Birth of the Clinic*. London: Routledge.
Foucault, M. (1999) *Madness and Civilization*. London: Routledge.
Freilich, M. (ed.) (1970) *Marginal Natives: Anthropologists at Work*. New York: Harper and Row.
Fuller, L. (1966) 'An afterword: science and the judicial process'. *Harvard Law Review*, 79, pp. 1604–27.
Fulop, N. (1995) 'Involuntary outpatient civil commitment'. *International Journal of Law and Psychiatry*, 18 (3), pp. 291–303.

Gask, L., Sibbald, B. and Creed, F. (1997) 'Evaluating models of working at the interface between mental health services and primary care'. *British Journal of Psychiatry*, 170, pp. 6–11.

Goffman, E. (1980) *Asylums*. Harmondsworth: Penguin.

Gold, R. (1958) 'Roles in sociological field observations'. *Social Forces*, 36, pp. 217–23.

Goldberg, D. and Gournay, K. (1966) 'The general practitioner, the psychiatrist and the burden of mental health care'. *Maudsley Discussion Paper No. 1*.

Goldfinger, S., Schutt, R., Turner, W. *et al.* (1996) 'Assessing homeless mentally ill persons for permanent housing: screening for safety'. *Community Mental Health Journal*, 3 June, 32 (3), pp. 275–88.

Gostin, L. (1975) *A Human Condition, I, The Mental Health Act from 1959 to 1975*. London: MIND.

Gostin, L. (1980) 'Mental health service tribunals'. *British Medical Journal*, 25 October, 281, pp. 1142–3.

Greenland, C. (1970) *Mental Illness and Civil Liberty*. Birkenhead: Willmer Bros.

Greenberg, A. and Bailey, J. (1994) 'The irrelevance of the medical model of mental illness to law and ethics'. *International Journal of Law and Psychiatry*, 17 (2), pp. 153–73.

Gross, M. (1999) 'Ethics education and physician morality'. *Social Science and Medicine*, 49, pp. 329–42.

Guarnaccia, P. and Parra, P. (1996) 'Ethnicity, social status, and families' experiences of caring for a mentally ill family member'. *Community Mental Health Journal*, 3 June, 31 (3), pp. 243–59.

Gwyn, R. and Elwyn, G. (1999) 'When is a shared decision not (quite) a shared decision?' *Social Science & Medicine*, 49, pp. 437–47.

Hammersley, M. (1989) *The Dilemma of Qualitative Method: Herbert Blumer and the Chicago tradition*. London, Routledge.

Hammersley, M. and Atkinson, P. (1983) *Ethnography: principles in practice*. London: Tavistock.

Hare, E. (1998) *On the History of Lunacy: the 19th Century and After*. London: Gabbay.

Harris, E. and Barraclough, B. (1997) 'Suicide as an outcome for mental disorders'. *British Journal of Psychiatry*, 170, pp. 205–28.

Hastie, R. (ed.) (1993) *Inside the Juror*. Cambridge: Cambridge University Press.

Hawkins, K. (ed.) (1992) *The Uses of Discretion*. Oxford: Clarendon Press.

Hepworth, D. (1983a) 'The decision process of the Mental Health Review Tribunal – 1. Review of literature and research'. *Medicine Science and the Law*, 23 (2), pp. 131–41.

Hepworth, D. (1983b) 'The decision process of the Mental Health Review Tribunal – 2. Analysis of research findings'. *Medicine Science and the Law*, 23 (3), pp. 171–82.

Hobbs, D. and May, T. (ed.) (1993) *Interpreting the Field*. Oxford: Clarendon Press.

Hogarth, J. (1971) *Sentencing as a Human Process*. Toronto: University of Toronto Press.

Hoggett, B. (1990) *Mental Health Law*, 3rd edn. London: Sweet & Maxwell.

Hoggett, B. (1996) *Mental Health Law*. London: Sweet & Maxwell, p. 201.

Howell, S. (ed.) (1995) *Mental Health Review Tribunal News Sheet* London: DOH

HSG (94)5 *Introduction of Supervision Registers for Mentally Ill People from 1 April 1994*. NHS Executive.

Jarman, B., Hirsch, S., White, P. and Driscoll, R. (1992) 'Predicting psychiatric admission rates'. *British Medical Journal*, 2 May, 304, pp. 1146–51.

Jones, K. (1980) 'The Limitations of the legal approach to mental health'. *International Journal of Law and Psychiatry*, 3, pp. 1–15.

Jones, R. (1996) *Mental Health Act Manual*, 5th edn. London: Sweet & Maxwell.

Jones, R. (1997) *Mental Health Act Manual*. London: Sweet and Maxwell.

Leggatt, A. (2001) *Report of the Review of Tribunals. Tribunals for Users – One System, One Service*. London: Lord Chancellors Department.

Kendell, R. (1993) 'Diagnosis and classification'. In *Companion to Psychiatric Studies*. Eds R. Kendell and A. Zealley. London: Churchill Livingstone.

Konecni, V. and Ebbesen, E. (1984) 'The mythology of legal decision making'. *International Journal of Law and Psychiatry*, 7, pp. 5–18.

Langley, G. (1993) 'Mental Health Review Tribunals in practice'. *Psychiatric Bulletin*, 17, pp. 331–6.

Leggatt, A. (2001) 'Report of the review of tribunals. Tribunals for users – one system, one service'. London: Lord Chancellors Department.

Litwack, T. (1996) '"Dangerous" patients: a survey of one forensic facility and review of the issue'. *Aggression and Violent Behavior*, 1 (2), pp. 97–122.

Maynard, A. (1996) 'Financing and paying for care in schizophrenia'. *Handbook of Mental Health Economics and Health Policy*, 1, pp. 423–31.

McDonald, A. (1995) 'The Mental Health Act 1983 – treatment, restraint and appeals to Mental Health Review Tribunals'. *Elders*, 4 (2), pp. 41–7.

McDonald, A. and Taylor, M. (1995) 'The Mental Health Act 1983 – discharge from hospital'. *Elders*, 4 (3), pp. 36–44.

McDonald, A. and Taylor, M. (1995) 'The Mental Health Act 1983 – the application of the Act: admission to hospital and emergency intervention'. *Elders*, 4 (1), pp. 27–35.

McKinlay, J., Potter, D. and Feldman, H. (1996) 'Non-medical influences on medical decision-making'. *Social Science Medicine*, 42 (5), pp. 769–76.

Mental Health Act Commission (1998) *The Threshold for Admission and the Relapsing Patient*. Nottingham: MHAC.

Mental Health Review Tribunals for England and Wales (1996) *Annual Report 1995*. London: HMSO.

Miller, J. (1970) *Professional Decision-Making*. New York: Praeger.

Monahan, J. and Steadman, H. (eds) (1994) *Violence and Mental Disorder*. Chicago: University of Chicago Press.

Mullen, P. (1999) 'Dangerous people with severe personality disorder'. *British Medical Journal*, 30 October, 319, pp. 1146–7.

Myers, D. (1997) 'Mental health review tribunals. A follow-up of reviewed patients'. *British Journal of Psychiatry*, March, 170, pp. 253–6.

Nicholson, R., Ekenstam, C. and Norwood, S. (1996) 'Coercion and the outcome of psychiatric hospitalisation'. *International Journal of Law and Psychiatry*, 19 (2), pp. 201–17.

North, C., Ritchie, J. and Ward, K. (1993) *Factors Influencing the Implementation of the Care Programme Approach*. London: HMSO.

O'Brien, T., Mellsop, G., McDonald, K. and Ruthe, C. (1995) 'A one year analysis of appeals made to mental health review tribunals in New Zealand'. *Australian and New Zealand Journal of Psychiatry*, 29 (4), pp. 661–5.

Parliamentary debates (*Hansard*) House of Commons Official Report. London: HMSO.

Payne, S. (1995) 'The rationing of psychiatric beds: changing trends in sex-ratios in admission to psychiatric hospital'. *Health and Social Care in the Community*, 3 (5), pp. 289–300.

Peay, J. (1982) 'Mental Health Review Tribunals and the Mental Health (Amendment) Act'. *Criminal Law Review*, pp. 794–808.

Peay, J. (1989) *Tribunals on Trial*, Oxford: Clarendon.

Peay, J. and Shapland, J. (1982) 'Introduction'. *International Journal of Law and Psychiatry*, 15, pp. 125–8.

Pilgrim, D. and Rogers, A. (1997) *A Sociology of Mental Health & Illness*. Buckingham: Open University Press.

Plous, S. (1993) *The Psychology of Judgment and Decision Making*. New York: McGraw-Hill.

Prins, H. (1997) 'Editorial: personal liberties versus public safety: some issues for Mental Health Review Tribunals (MHRTs)'. *Medicine Science Law*, 37 (1), pp. 2–3.

Report of the Committee on Administrative Tribunals and Enquiries (Chairman The Rt Hon Sir Oliver Franks, GCMG KCB CBE); Cmnd 218, July 1957.

Report of the Expert Committee (1999) *Review of the Mental Health Act 1983*. London: Department of Health.

Richardson, G. (1999) 'The impact of judicial review on the mental health review tribunal'. ESRC Report R000237006.

Richardson, G. and Machin, D. (2000) 'Doctors on Tribunals: a confusion of roles'. *British Journal of Psychiatry*, 176, pp. 110–15.

Ritchie, J., Dick, D. and Lingham, R. (1994) *The Report of the Inquiry into the Care and Treatment of Christopher Clunis*. London: HMSO.

Roberts, J. (1913) *Stone's Justices' Manual 45th Edition*. London: Butterworth.

Roberts, J. (1916) *The Metropolitan Police Guide 6th Edition*. London: HMSO.

Ross, L., Lepper, M. and Hubbard, M. (1975) 'Perseverance in self-perception: Biased attributional processes in the debriefing paradigm'. *Journal of Personality and Social Psychology*, 32, pp. 880–92.

Royal Commission (1957) *Report of the Commission on the Law relating to Mental Illness and Mental Deficiency 1954–1957* (The Percy Commission). Cmnd 169. London: HMSO.

Schauer, F. (1992) *Playing by the Rules*, Oxford: Clarendon Press.

Shaw, J., Appleby, L., Amos, T. *et al.* (1999) 'Mental disorder and clinical care in people convicted of homicide: national clinical survey'. *British Medical Journal*, 8 May, 318, pp. 1240–4.

Silverman, D. (1993) *Interpreting Qualitative Data: Methods for analysing talk, text and interaction*. London: Sage.

Silverman, D. (ed.) (1998) *Qualitative Research*. London: Sage.

Simon, F. (1971) *Research Methods in Criminology*. Research Study No. 7, London: HMSO.

Smit, J. (1987) 'Question or quarrel: an analysis of the dialogue between judge and patient in the involuntary commitment procedure'. *International Journal of Law and Psychiatry*, 10, pp. 251–63.

Szasz, T. (1974) *Law, Liberty, and Psychiatry*. London: Routledge & Keegan Paul.

Taylor, P. and Monahan, J. (1996) 'Commentary: dangerous patients or dangerous diseases?' *British Medical Journal*, 13 April, 312, pp. 967–9.

Tidmarsh, D. (1997) 'Psychiatric risk, safety cultures and homicide inquiries'. *The Journal of Forensic Psychiatry*, May, 8 (1), pp. 138–51.

Turner, B. (1992) *Regulating Bodies*. London: Routledge.

Tyrer, P. (1999) 'The national service framework: a scaffold for mental health'. *British Medical Journal*, 16 October, 319, pp. 1017–18.

Unsworth, C. (1987) *The Politics of Mental Health Legislation*. Oxford: Clarendon.

van Koppen, P. (1999) 'A comparison of the use of psychological scientific evidence'. *Paper presented at International Conference on Psychology and Law, Dublin*, 6–10 July.

Wade, H. and Forsyth, C. (1982) *Administrative Law*. Oxford: Clarendon.

Wadham, J. and Mountfield, H. (1999) *Blackstone's Guide to the Human Rights Act 1998.* London: Blackstone Press Limited.

Wagenaar, W., van Koppen, P. and Crombag, H. (1993) *Anchored Narratives.* Hemel Hempstead: Harvester Wheatsheaf.

Wilkinson, P. and Sharpe, M. (1993) 'What happens to patients discharged by Mental Health Review Tribunals?' *Psychiatric Bulletin*, 17, pp. 337–8.

Wood, J. (1970) 'Mental Health Review Tribunals'. *Medicine Science and the Law*, 10, pp. 86–92.

Wood, J. (1993) 'Reform of the Mental Health Act 1983'. *British Journal of Psychiatry*, 162, pp. 14–22.

Wood, J. (1995) 'The challenge of individual rights'. *British Journal of Psychiatry*, 166. pp. 417–20.

Yarmey, A., Jacob, J. and Porter, A. (1999) 'Effects of a culprit's demeanor on witness recall and duration estimation'. *Poster presented at International Conference on Psychology and Law, Dublin*, 6–10 July.

Index